Rhythm

FOR RAIN

JOHN LOUW NELSON

WITH ILLUSTRATIONS

BOSTON

HOUGHTON MIFFLIN COMPANY

The Riverside Press Cambridge

1937

The Riverside Press
CAMBRIDGE · MASSACHUSETTS
PRINTED IN THE U.S.A.

THIS BOOK IS DEDICATED TO
MY MOTHER
HARRIET SCHUYLER NELSON
WITH ALL MY LOVE
AND
AS A PRESENT FOR HER
SEVENTY-FIFTH BIRTHDAY
FEBRUARY 27, 1937

PREFACE

THE patterned design of a book is like a textile's weft, and, similarly, behind it is the strong, tested invisible warp that gave it being. In *Rhythm for Rain* this unseen framework is the loyalty, faith, and courage of my family and of my friends.

For that I am eternally grateful — in my memory of Mary Austin, who started me on my Indian trail; in my thought of Mrs. Harold L. Ickes, who directed my steps into ceremonial byways; to the Indian artists Kabotie, Quoyavema (who is also the Kwayeshva of the photographs) and Mootzka, who worked for me for many years and added to my own endeavor the rich substance of their talents; to Mrs. Oliver Harriman and Princess Pignatelli, sterling friends from my boyhood; to Mrs. Harold D. Corbusier whose generous aid can never be sufficiently acknowledged; to Mrs. Fred Totzke for her unswerving devotion to my family for over thirty years; to the precious memory of my father, a Bishop for nearly three decades and a lover of beauty and simple faith all his life; above all, I owe most to my mother and to my wife who have walked by my side without fear or reproach down the steep path to deprivation in order that my work and this book might come to be.

As to the pattern itself — all my life I have been a musician; concerts and composing were my central activities for nearly twenty years. Still, from the time when, as a boy of fourteen, I orated as Logan before Lord Baltimore

— on which occasion Doctor John H. Finley, who has stood by me loyally in recent years, was one of the judges who awarded the elocution prize to another boy — always there has been an enharmonic Indian melody rising and falling in my life until finally it burst into full song in Northern Arizona.

However, the story of my ten years with the Hopi Indians must be told elsewhere except as it discloses the background for *Rhythm for Rain*

From the time when first I saw the Katchinas dance, I knew that the pounded rhythm of their footsteps was an echoed tapping from the ancient past; an insistent message summoning forth something in me as well as calling together the rain clouds for the mating of sky and earth.

So through the still heat of many summers again and again I saw the gods dance for rain. From the time the sun rose until it had buried itself behind the coned sacredness of the west, I had watched the masked men leaping in prayer to the greater gods of the four worlds. I had seen the sweat ooze out of the tiny eye-holes of their masks just as they prayed that the hidden waters would emerge from the drying rock and sand. I had seen the men press their blistering feet on the stove-hot rock of the mesa crest and, incredibly, I had seen the rain called forth from the 'yellow' north and had felt its driving force sweeping out of the whitened east. In the face of such elemental faith and victory, what could I do but accept the sincerity and be awed by the courage of men who challenged the summer-burned sun and defied the upthrust heat of the seared dry sand?

Likewise in winter I knew the pulse of midnight prayer

in the secret rooms below the earth. I saw dignity — fantastically conceived — embody in human form the majesty of the sun as Ahöla, gave the blessing of the sky to prevent or cure all human ills. I knew then, too, the sub-zero freeze of northern blasts that could never lure a shiver to the bare bodies of those who planted their feathered sticks of prayer.

So the years passed while I let this ancient life and faith flow into my own being and then, gradually, I began to sense inner impulses that clamored for release; for form, for life beyond my own. So writing began; first as detailed accounts of ritual and legend until, unexpectedly, from the last survivor of the drought of eighty years ago I heard the stripped horror of that time when for not one year, but for two and for part of a third year, the cloud gods lived in a distant land and could not be lured back to the fields of the Hopi men. When my aged friend had shared with me her final memory of that time, I knew that I had touched drama such as the world has seldom seen — not just the external drama of drought, but the epic tragedy of the apparent futility of faith in the ancient gods whose being is the inherited symbol of life and hope to an entire race; the amassed inheritance of a thousand years. In the drought that crept close to a final sweep of annihilation there was a challenge to the collective tribal soul.

So out of my eager questionings *Rhythm for Rain* came into being. In it is no incident or thought or belief that has not occurred or lived in the minds of these desert Indians. I have invented nothing; even the blind epileptic is a figure borrowed from legend. My greatest hope is that I have been able to show the Indian as he lives most richly:

in the guarded, venerated faith of his fathers. Those who have known only the outer Indian have never known him at all, for his real life and nature lie in the subconscious, intuitive realm that comes to the surface in his faith, in his art, and in his philosophy of life.

Some of the pictures are reproduced from the paintings of my gifted Indian artist-aids. Each of them is the final record of years of seeing, sketching, noting, and recording. In some cases eight years passed before the last details could be secured. Some day I hope to be able to present these and other such pictures in all the glory of their natural color.

The remaining illustrations are scenes from the motion-picture record that I made two years ago when I reconstructed the life of a vanished age by importing a truckful of blankets and ceremonial garments from a New York Museum. Thus, for a few days or hours I replaced the modern calicoes, overalls, and Czecho-Slovakian shawls with the simple beauty of the Hopi native weaves. And in that experience is there not the very essence of irony? To lend the Indian for a brief moment the robes into which his ancestors wove the distillations of the spirit; the garnered beauty of a people who gather color with the eagerness of the dry earth absorbing rain.

CONTENTS

I. TWICE BORN

As SIKYANÖMSI already had brought six nut-brown babies into the world, the imminent arrival of the seventh did not disturb her very much. She moved about the house with ponderous grace and prepared mutton stew for her husband and the three children whose feet had stayed on the path of life.

When their desires had been satisfied, 'Nömsi lowered her heavy body to the hard, dirt-covered floor and sat near the open doorway. Automatically, her fingers reached for the split yucca strands, dyed with soft vegetable colors, and with swift sureness she coiled them about the protruding end of the bunched prairie hay that gave substance and strength to her basket.

While her hands instinctively reached for the needed colors to work out an elaborate design, her mind floated back to the son who had fingered feebly at her breasts a year ago, and then been drawn back to the spirit world.

She knew that he had been too little to go to the skeleton house of the dead, where Massauh, their grim god, moves about clanking his necklace of bones. She knew that his tiny soul had lingered near her hearth waiting to be reborn.

All through that winter, before retiring at night, she had taken a small portion of food and placed it in the open room where his invisible spirit could inhale its essence. So, through all those windblown months, the presence of this unseen child had been quite as definite a reality to Sikyanömsi as the noise-making, fun-loving girls who dashed in and out of the house, restless with the vigor of their youth.

While happiness had come to Sikyanömsi through the belief that her boy was to be reborn, still nothing had been left to chance. It might be that the soul of some other infant, maybe a girl, would try to force its way into the body that so soon was to be born, and thus compel the boy's spirit to remain outside in the world of constant shadow. Then, too, the Indian woman knew that she was beginning to get old; that quite possibly this seventh infant would be her very last. So, to make the coming of this boy an absolute certainty, she had eaten some leaves from the *lolimuh* plant, the one that governs the birth of boys, and as she chewed the bitter herb, she felt with a rush of happiness that she had aided her son in his effort to return to her and to take his part in a life ruled by the sun and marked with joyous dancing.

The plain, square face of the forty-year-old Hopi woman glowed with the anticipation of one who awaits the fulfillment of a great desire. Her fingers, trained to act independently of her thoughts, kept on plucking the split yucca strands — yellow, green, brown, or black — and, expertly handled, the pattern grew, while her thought soared upward, serene as an eagle, wheeling above an everyday world.

Footsteps were heard, so she looked through the door and saw on the trail the short, fat figure of her mother, plodding along through the thick, dry sand. The woman's face was slightly flushed below the tumpline cotton rag that held on her back the earthenware jug, dripping with water from the spring below. Breathing deeply, she waddled into the house, lugging the heavy, smooth-worn pot. Then, when she had laid it on the floor, with a sigh she straightened her aching back and turned to look appraisingly at her daughter. There was no need of questioning: she knew that Sikyanömsi would tell her when the final pains began.

As all seemed well, the grandmother bustled about the room and was ready to serve the evening meal when her son-in-law and the girls returned. 'Nömsi tucked in a final strand, then put away her basket work, rose heavily to her feet, and poked about; a bit more bread, some fresh hot meat were added to the supper on the floor, while Letaiyo, her husband, munched away, although his eyes followed 'Nömsi's form as she moved awkwardly about the room. The rebirth of a son meant much to him, but the routine acts of life need not be changed.

The sun set with an orange flame, and for a time the desert was a purple-bordered land streaked with brilliant light. Then the final red glowed and paled, and vanished in the suddenness of night. The girls romped out to the darkening street and to the house of an aunt, while Letaiyo went out also and the women were alone.

An hour passed, and then the calm, brown face of Sikyanömsi slowly turned to gray as the rhythmic surge of mounting pain twisted her inmost being. Still the time was not yet come for her to be alone; to endure in solitude the final act of birth.

The grandmother watched and gauged the time while

the cedar-fed flames danced away in the corner of the room, and outside some small, gray burro shrieked his eternal woe to the twinkle of the stars.

As her pains swept in with the roll of resistless tide, 'Nömsi crawled to the bed of sand that her mother had spread out on the floor, and with her head bowed she knelt there, motionless. The old woman, Sowüchti, looked about to make certain that the juniper that must be chewed, the little broom, and other necessaries were at hand. With a stubby, wrinkled thumb, she pointed at each one and seemed to count. Then, satisfied that all were there, she turned and left the room. Outside she stood, quite near the door, while her ears grew tense with listening for the sound that would permit her to return—the sound of the shrill protest of a newborn child.

Within, the flames grew lazy on the hearth and great beads of sweat on the mother's face gleamed in its flickering light. Her hands were clenched with effort to resist each surge of pain. Then, feeling the need for greater strength, she raised her head and looked upward toward the roof, where her eyes caught a glimpse of a tiny piece of brown fur hanging from the thatch. As she looked at it, a smile of confidence banished for a moment the pain-constricted lines from her face. Pivani, the weasel, was there, that most skilled of burrowing animals. His little fur hung high above her head, and his spirit would be with the child, aiding him to tunnel his way out into the world.

A few minutes later a thin, high-pitched cry brought the grandmother hurrying back into the room, and through all the mists of 'Nömsi's pain-dazed mind, as she yielded her body to the ministrations of her mother, one thought gleamed like a brilliant sun-shaft: she had been right; her son had come forth from the world of shadow.

Skillfully, a short piece of the mother's hair string, which had been woven from Sikyanömsi's coal-black locks, was tied about the umbilical cord, close to the infant's body. Then this cord was cut against the hard wooden shaft of an arrow. Sikyanömsi was certain that on reaching manhood her son would become a great hunter; but to ensure this it would be necessary to wrap a piece of this severed cord around the arrow and then to thrust its shaft into the thatch of the ceiling and leave it there, so that during the long years to maturity its influence would strengthen her son, develop his skill, and make him one of the great hunters and fighters of his tribe.

A few minutes later Honanwüchti, the baby's paternal grandmother, being summoned, hurried into the room; for there were many important rites that could be attended to only by a member of the father's clan. First the baby was carefully washed with purifying suds made from pounded yucca root. Then, when he had been dried, evil-dispelling, hair-preventing ashes were patted all over his minute, wrinkled body. When all this had been done, Honanwüchti strapped the child to his newly made cradle-board. And then, his physical needs having been cared for, she proceeded to attend to those essential rites that would safeguard his soul.

For twenty days the baby would be in constant danger from malevolent beings; so, to make certain that his spirit would remain there during this time, the grandmother made four parallel lines on each of the walls, using for this purpose the finest kind of ground meal. In this way she built a house for the newborn infant, and she was sure no evil ghost could come beyond those lines.

Shortly after this precautionary rite had been attended to, Letaiyo, the father, came back to the room. He walked to the cradle and lifted away the cloth that completely covered it and the child. For a moment he looked at the minute, ruddy creature that he had fathered. Then, replacing the cloth, he turned to his wife.

'*Lolomai* — *pas lolomai* it is well,' he said.

And Sikyanömsi, flooded with contentment, beamed with joy. '*Wi* — yes, it is my little Tiposi who has come back again.'

All through the night that followed, Letaiyo kept watch over the fire in order that it might burn steadily, for under no circumstances must it be allowed to die. In that case, a bad spirit would enter his son's heart and fire would always have an evil hold on his life.

Before dawn, Sowüchti with the assistance of her son-in-law, placed before the door of the house a cotton robe stretched between two poles, in order that no ray of sun might be permitted to fall upon the infant boy. Tawa, the Sun, Great Father of all, is so powerful, so inconceivably great, that a newborn child must be purified, strengthened, and in every way prepared to receive the blessing of his rays.

Early in the morning of the fifth day, 'Nömsi carefully scraped away the meal from the lowest of the four lines on the walls. Then, taking these particles of corn meal in her hand, she walked out to the eastern ledge of the mesa just in time to meet the rising sun. With quiet seriousness she touched the meal with her lips and breathed into it a silent prayer to Tawa to illumine her boy's face, and finally, being filled with the strength from his rays, for him to fall asleep in old age. Then she tossed the meal toward the eastern horizon, where the sun's 'forehead' was rising over a distant mesa.

On the tenth and fifteenth days the second and third lines of meal were cast with prayer to the sun, and finally, when the twentieth day dawned, the curtain, placed before the door, was rolled and put away.

The white light of first dawn made the figures of Honanwüchti and Letaiyo's sisters barely visible as they hurried down the rock-rutted street and into the house where the baby slept. The paternal grandmother carried in readiness yucca roots and water. First the mashed roots were beaten into the water until a mountain of foam arose from the level of the large bowl in which it had been placed. Then from beside the infant's cradle Honanwüchti took two perfect ears of whitest corn which she had placed by the child the day of his birth.

The gray-haired grandmother dipped the corn ears into the suds, and after they had been washed ceremonially, 'Nömsi knelt before the bowl and let her long, black hair fall into the soapy water. Swiftly but solemnly the woman washed the mother's head and then those of the other women. When their hair was dry, Honanwüchti took the baby from his cradle, washed him with yucca suds, then patted him all over with sacred corn meal, a few particles of which were also put in his mouth. Then the first of the aunts, who were kneeling in a circle on the floor, took the corn 'mother' ears and with her right hand placed them over the baby's breast while in a low voice she whispered the ritual: 'Until old age may you be protected, and Kwayeshva are you named.'

Her sisters then in turn repeated the ancient formula, and each one gave to the boy a different name. It was expected, of course, that most of these names would be dropped and only one 'stick' until his final ceremonial initiation when he became a man.

The misty light of early dawn was becoming vibrant with color when the final protective line of meal was scraped away from all the walls and the grandmother, carrying the child, was followed by the other women to the eastern ledge of the mesa, just as the sun was about to rise.

A thousand feet below them lay the shadow-bound desert, an undulating plane through which buttes and mesas thrust themselves abruptly upward. Unending space — the vastness of an isolated world and a few quiet women with a newborn child, mere dots on the summit of a huge, sheer-sided cliff, while in the east the slow, steady sweep of the sun rolled back the darkness. Like an advancing tide it rippled down the chiseled rocks towering above the people, and then slowly it crept across the rocky ledge on which they stood until it touched the tiny boy.

Intensely solemn, the grandmother placed the corn ears again against the baby's breast, and this time waved them to the sun, thus giving their child to the supreme god whose rays would protect him through his life. Carefully the old woman enumerated the names by which the baby might be known. Then, as they walked quietly along the trail back to the mother's home, the sun, rising clear above the distant mesa, swept through the town in a sudden flood of gleaming, blazing light.

Twice BORN

For the boy Kwayeshva, life as an individual member of his tribe had dawned with the sun. He had been presented to Tawa, the father of all creation, and now, if death should drag him into the skeleton world of shadows, there could be no rebirth.

II. HOW THE BUGS WERE BAFFLED

THE mounting sun of mid-April had drawn all the frost out of the ground; then in May, the brittle sticks of the sage and greasewood bushes that dotted the desert landscape were profusely decorated with leaves of almost translucent green. To the west the Snow-High-Place, Növatükyaovi, where the gods have their homes, stood out as cones of austere whiteness against a cobalt sky.

Sikyanömsi sat in front of her adobe house at the extreme southern tip of the village of Mishongnovi. Happiness danced within her veins and sparkled from her eyes like the sun-touched air that flowed past the Giant's Chair in the south. So she basked in the even flow of warmth and let her mind take wing. Her body had regained its normal strength and her son was a healthy, hungry mite with tousled, thick black hair.

So 'Nömsi felt that the widespread world, from the blue of Shötüknanguh, who strides across the sky, to the deepest depths where Muyingwuh works and pushes up the green, was a land that made her tingle with the richness of its joy. Birds dipped from the clouds and snatched at fluttering morsels in the air. Squirrels made emergence from the rocks and flicked their tails in whimsy or excitement. Even the burro seemed to sense the vigor of the day and tried to unloose his hobble and go adventuring.

But Sikyanömsi was quite well aware that all this scene

that flooded her with so much satisfaction had not just come about through chance, but was the reward that was her due. In fact, she reflected with complacence, she herself was responsible for much of it. The snow that had been transmuted to growing corn had been brought by the dancing prayer of men and the grinding-stones of women; for food is quite essential as an offering to the gods.

Then, too, her own deep inner joy in her sturdy son Kwayeshva had been earned by constant care. One must be on guard, she knew quite well, and anticipate all need. The voracious appetite of her small son, the way he mauled her breasts and clamored for his mother's milk, had made her fear that maybe she could not satisfy his need. This fear had grown to worry, and with this nervous doubt the supply of the needed fluid had diminished and the howls of 'Yeshva in proportion had increased.

Here, then, was a problem to be met; and had she solved it? Why, of course, in the most successful way. She had told her man to search about for leaves of *pi'inya* plant. It had been hard to find them, too, for the spring was just begun. But Letaiyo brought home at least some little leaves and stalks, and she had eaten the milk-exuding greens and been quite well aware that as like always produces like, she would take unto herself the properties of the plant, and as a result be able to satisfy completely the needs of her small son. Which is exactly what had happened: she had ceased to worry, the milk from her breasts flowed freely, and Kwayeshva grew fat.

It was such a source of deep satisfaction to the Hopi woman to feel the tangible reality of her baby tugging determinedly at her breasts after the long year in which she had endeavored to feed his invisible spirit with particles of food placed in the open room. A happy smile edged her lips as her thoughts became retrospective of those months of confident preparation.

A shrill cry from within interrupted her reverie, so 'Nömsi hurried into the room and picked up the cloth-enveloped cradle. With an accustomed motion she bared a breast, and presently 'Yeshva was feeding, noisily and with content. Then, after this meal had been finished, even though 'Nömsi dandled her child, he cooed and gurgled and made it perfectly obvious that he had no intention whatever of going to sleep again.

A clattering noise was heard from outside the door, and as 'Nömsi poked her head out to see what caused it, she saw her father-in-law, Makya, dismounting from an almost white furry burro. The old man hobbled the animal's front legs with an old cotton rag and looked toward the house.

'*Yungya'ai* — come in,' his daughter called to him. Then, as he crossed the threshold, '*Öm hinchaki* — what are you doing?' she asked.

Makya made a sweeping gesture with his arm which indicated that he had just come from the cornfields. Hearing sounds from the completely covered cradle, he removed the cotton cloth and with his squinting, gray old eyes, he peered at his wakeful grandson.

'He won't sleep,' 'Nömsi complained. 'All day he stays awake. I feed him till he is fat like some prairie dog, but still he is not sleepy.'

The old man's wrinkled face grew thoughtful for a moment. Then, as an idea occurred to him, 'I can get you something, maybe something that will make him sleep,' he declared, and a pleased expression softened the seeming harshness of his face.

'That bat that flies when it is dark,' he said. 'He likes to sleep all day. I know some plants that look just like those bats and have leaves big like their wings. I will get you leaves from those bat plants, then with them you must make some tea. Give 'Yeshva bath with that warm tea and he will sleep all day.'

This suggestion delighted the Hopi mother, so as she wanted the plants immediately the old man hurried out and unhobbled his burro. In a few moments his head and shoulders disappeared behind the sand hill as the animal made its sure-footed way down the winding trail.

'Yeshva, unaware of the orgy of sleep that was in store for him through the efficacy of the bat-plant, decided at this point that he was being neglected. So a wail of strong-minded protest announced his views. Then suddenly the wail became a duet of lamentation. On top of that a trio could be heard. Sikyanömsi, changing her ideas about the peacefulness of the world, rushed frantically in through the door.

Her son wept in the invisibility of the cradle-board. The youngest girl, Kwavöhuh, or Eagle-Breast-Feather, was making rivulets of tears run through red and black daubs of paint that streaked her face. Something was being clutched tightly in her arms, and her next older sister, Flute Girl, was shouting with all the defiance of angry six years of age and at the same time twisting the littlest one's fingers in an effort to pry loose the treasure that was being guarded. The oldest girl, Kwamana, stood by, semi-maternal in her effort to separate the children, but at the same time enjoying hugely the spectacle of their fight.

'Nömsi yanked the aggressive one away from the smallest girl, and at once all three broke into an excited clamor of explanation. All through it 'Yeshva howled, completely disregarded.

The mother surveyed them grimly. 'Now what makes you fight?' she demanded.

The six-year-old managed to make herself heard. 'She took my doll — that *Hahai'ih* Katchinas gave me in Bean Dance.'

Sikyanömsi disengaged the clenched hands of Kwavöhuh, and found in them a demure-faced doll whose red, black, and white body was streaked from the wet of tears. Slowly, reprovingly she shook her head at the abashed little one.

'You must not take your sister's doll,' she scolded. 'How would you like if maybe some woman took you away from me? Those dolls that our gods gave you are your babies, and each girl has her own. Where is your doll?' she then asked.

'She can't find it,' the oldest child informed her. 'Maybe it is lost.'

'If she has lost her doll,' the mother announced, 'then she is bad. And maybe when she is big then she will lose her babies, too.' With this ominous suggestion she handed the doll to its rightful owner. 'You children must be good,' she declared. 'Soon your father will be home, and if you make fuss and don't help your mother cook some food, then maybe there will be no supper and your father will be mad.'

Somewhat awed by this possibility, Kwamana went over to the fire and picked up a stick of wood. As she did so she caught sight of a spot of green underneath the cedar logs that stood beside the hearth. Reaching down between the twisted sticks, she groped about for a moment and then triumphantly pulled out the missing doll.

'See,' she said to the baby. 'Here is your Tewa girl. Maybe she tried to hide from you.'

The little Kwavöhuh began to laugh at this funny idea. Then, taking the doll from her sister, she clutched it happily, and so peace was restored.

Sikyanömsi, with the girls' quarrel straightened out, picked up the completely distraught Kwayeshva, fed him to approximate happiness, and then concentrated her thought on the preparation of food. A few minutes later, large round cakes of frying bread were being puffed up to the bursting point as they cooked in boiling sheep's fat in an earthen dish. The oldest daughter cleared away some of the mess from the floor, and a few moments later Letaiyo, the father, entered the room, lugging his white-man's saddle, of which he was enormously proud, for it was the only one in the village.

As soon as 'Nömsi had finished frying the bread, she placed it on the floor with a bowl of mutton and hominy. Then she pulled a few sheepskins out from the pile by the wall, and on these the family sat so that they formed a circle around the food.

Again the door opened, and in waddled the bow-legged Sowüchti, the grandmother. As usual, the old woman was out of breath from climbing the steep trail with a heavy jar of water on her back. Leaving the door open, she unwrapped her pot and took a long drink of the cool liquid from the spring.

'Aaah!' she exclaimed with satisfaction; she wiped her mouth noisily on her arm, and then lurched her fat body to the sheepskins where the other members of the family were squatting cross-legged before the evening meal. Presently they were all dipping their index fingers into the common pot that was filled with the hot, succulent stew, and were eating with much relish. Generous portions of the fried bread were broken off from time to time and dipped into the warm juices of the meat and corn. A few dried peaches that had been stewed to appetizing softness completed the meal. Then Letaiyo threw himself down on other sheepskins by the hearth, and puffing on a corn-husk cigarette of native tobacco, he jiggled the baby's cradle with his foot.

A scrawny yellow dog poked his head in the door and sniffed at the remains of the tempting stew. Then, seeing that the people were occupied elsewhere, he crept over to the bowl and with ecstatic pleasure began gulping down the largest pieces of meat. Suddenly the grandmother spied the animal, and with a hissing '*Tcha — a*!' she waddled furiously toward the dog, which sent him scampering out through the door, near which he lingered, poking his head in hopefully from time to time.

Then, as courage returned, for some minutes the animal stood with his front paws on the threshold, sniffing into the room. His eagerness for food seemed to have deadened his sense of caution, so that he paid no attention to the sound of footsteps approaching from the street. All at once a red-moccasined foot made swift and painful contact with the dog's ribs. As the animal ran limping and howling down the road, Makya came toward the family and held out to Sikyanömsi the promised herbs which he had been gathering.

'What you got there?' Letaiyo inquired. So the gray-haired Makya explained the nature of the bat plant, and how being bathed with it would make Kwayeshva sleep contentedly through the daytime.

'*Ancha'ai, ancha'ai* — it is right,' the father exclaimed with high approval.

Early the next morning, as soon as she had fed her family, 'Nömsi stewed the leaves of the bat plant and then bathed her usually wakeful son with the tea-colored liquid. Perhaps it may have been due to the magic properties of the plant, but it is possible that it was the novel sensation of being bathed with a warm liquid that made him drowsy. At any rate, a few moments later, while his mother watched excitedly, Kwayeshva's little black eyes closed in sleep. All morning long, until he awoke clamorous for food, the house was unusually quiet as the baby slept swathed in cotton cloth and strapped to his covered cradle-board.

That night, shortly after the family had gone to sleep — some of them on the roof of the house and the others inside — a shrill cry from the cradle woke the mother. Drowsily she rocked the strapped-down infant, then her own head gradually sank to her shoulder and she was just falling asleep when more howls from Kwayeshva opened her eyes and made her dandle the cradle again. And so it continued all through the night. Then when dawn came and with it light, a thoroughly weary 'Nömsi discovered that her baby's face was covered with red blotches. As she lifted the cradle, a minute, round, brown insect scuttled away toward the darkness. Later in the day, when Makya happened to go past the house on his burro, 'Nömsi called to him:

'That bat plant that you found is good. Our baby slept all day. Maybe though he slept too much. Last night those bedbugs, they made him mad. 'Yeshva does not like those bedbugs when they bite. So he cried all night and his mother did not sleep. Maybe you will get some plants that will make those bedbugs angry so they will go away.'

'*Wi, ancha'ai* — it is right; I will get some plants. You must tie these plants to 'Yeshva's cradle-board. Then those bedbugs they will all get mad and go away. Maybe then your baby will want to sleep.'

So that night Kwayeshva lay in an aromatic bower and while the herbs kept the bedbugs away, still the baby slept but little. For the day before he had been washed again with the bat plant and had also been tired from a sleepless night, so that his slumber had been continuous from morning until darkness came.

The following day Sikyanömsi, being persuaded that the bat plant was altogether too effective as a daytime sedative, decided to discontinue its use. For, she reasoned, as the bat is awake all night, undoubtedly Kwayeshva was taking unto himself this trait as well. While nocturnal activity may be all right for bats, it is not too good for babies and their hard-working mothers.

It happened that on this particular day the three older children were unusually noisy, which may in part account for the fact that Kwayeshva did not sleep so much during the sunlit hours. Then, being still surrounded by the wilted bug-proof greens, he, and therefore the whole family, slept soundly through the night.

III. A YEAR-OLD HUNTER TESTS HIS SKILL

When the pleasant warmth of spring had been followed by the remorseless heat of summer, Letaiyo had moved with his family to their summer ranch-house, six miles from the base of the mesa on which the village of Mishongnovi was built.

At the time of the first corn-planting, when with a planting stick he had poked kernels of corn into six-inch-deep holes, Letaiyo had thought nothing of running back and forth from the village to his distant field. Likewise when the delicate green blades of the corn were unsheathed, Letaiyo had made daily trips to the ranch in order that he might build tiny stone houses of small, flat rock around each tender plant, so that it might be protected from the relentless winds and cutting sands of spring.

But in summer there was much work to be done if he hoped to secure an abundant harvest. So it was within the one-room shack near the zealously guarded cornfields that Sikyanömsi nursed her baby during the intense heat of summer. The change of location had little effect on the nature of her daily work, for her family had to be fed, and beyond the time necessary for housework every possible moment must be spent in coiling plaques and baskets.

So 'Nömsi put her baby, strapped tight to the cradle-board, in the shade of the leafy branches of a peach tree that grew near her home. Then, after covering him over with a cloth to keep out flies, she resumed her daily work of basket-making. Perhaps her new-found happiness had made her unusually ambitious, but at any rate she had started to make a storage basket, bigger than any that hitherto ever had been made; and the design for this basket was to be a full-length figure of a Katchina. She had given careful thought to the question of which Katchina should be represented, for these masked gods of the Hopi are legion and their powers are varied. Without doubt the design should represent one of those that are beneficent and bring the clouds and rain; the others, who are always angry and have to be propitiated, would never do for her purpose.

Finally Sikyanömsi decided that she would weave into her basket, on each of its four sides, a figure of Angwusnasumtaka, one of the three great mothers of the gods, who comes each winter bearing a tray covered with the seeds of all the plants that are raised by the men for food and clothing. Underneath each of the figures of this crow-winged deity, 'Nömsi thought it would be effective to put triply executed cloud designs. There would be yellow ones for the north, white for the east, red for the south, and greenish blue for the west; for, as everyone knows, these are the colors that belong to the clouds of those directions. So as she planned it all, Sikyanömsi glowed with the thrill of a creator who embarks on the task of achieving a masterpiece.

While she was busily engaged in her work, Letaiyo came in from the cornfield and stood for a moment by the peach tree, looking appraisingly at the pendant fruit. He turned to his wife.

'In eight days, maybe, we shall have peaches,' he said to her, and there was a note of eager anticipation in his voice.

'*Ancha'ai* — it is well,' she answered. And then she told him of her ambitious plan to create a basket of superlative beauty and size. Letaiyo smiled and touched his wife's hair with his fingertips, and a deep sense of tenderness was in his touch.

Fall came, and the storage-room back of their living quarters in Mishongnovi was filled with corn, melons, and dried peaches in anticipation of their winter's need. To be sure, the melons were rather green, but in this condition they could be kept for a long time without spoiling in that dry desert air.

Winter swept down on the cliff dwellings of the Hopi, and the swirling masses of the snow brought joy to their hearts; for this is one form of precipitated moisture that does not roll away as do the sudden rains of summer.

As Kwayeshva's baby mind began to recognize the faces of those about him, his dawning consciousness became touched here and there with strange grotesque figures that danced or raced about. In fact one of them, wearing a huge buckskin for a cloak and with a tight-fitting yellow mask on his head, had leaned over the infant's cradle-board and placed a painted gourd rattle in his tiny outstretched hands. For weeks afterward the baby had banged against the covering arch of his cradle with his wonderful new toy, or had sucked at it contentedly until he had removed most of the paint, which didn't seem to hurt him in the least.

Another summer caused corn to mature in the Hopi

fields, and Kwayeshva, in a state of glorious nudity, toddled about, a young explorer in a world of fascinating adventure.

One day Letaiyo arrived at the ranch after a trip to Mishongnovi, and as he unsaddled his horse discovered Kwayeshva sitting in the middle of a large mud puddle — for there had been rain that afternoon. The child was splashing away in supreme contentment and making his little brown body several shades darker with a thick coat of mud.

'See, 'Yeshva,' Letaiyo called to him. 'I have *moos-hoya* — cat-little-one — for you to play with.'

Then as the boy stood up in the puddle and looked solemnly at his father, the latter unfastened a sack from his saddle and presently drew out a half-suffocated, almost paralyzed kitten. Out were stretched 'Yeshva's fat arms, but the kitten, eluding his grasp, limping, marched away, tail erect.

The small boy toddled after the animal and grasped it by the tail — for obviously this appendage was constructed as a convenient handle. Then all at once an angry howl brought Sikyanömsi to the door of the house. Letaiyo was laughing in high glee.

'It is Moosa that I get for 'Yeshva. 'Yeshva picks him up — so' — illustrating with pantomime — 'and then Moosa goes scratch like this ——' Another gesture showed the cause of the little boy's howling. As Kwayeshva by this time had recovered from his fright, the mother smiled unconcernedly and went back to her work of putting a green face on one of the crow-winged mothers who decorated her basket.

A sudden motion by the kitten attracted the child's attention and again he gave chase. A few moments later he was howling once more; and so, intermittently, he chased and howled all through the afternoon until by night he was covered with tiny scratches. His mother made one or two casual remarks about the small wounds, but was not particularly upset by them, for even a year-old hunter must suffer the hardships of the chase.

Ever since the preceding summer, Sikyanömsi had been working steadily, hour after hour, day after day, month after month, until, toward the second fall, her stupendous task was accomplished.

All through the length and breadth of Hopi, from the western village of Oraibi to the eastern foreign settlement of the Tewa, the news had spread about this basket, that was so large that if its maker stood inside all that could be seen of her would be her dark brown eyes peering over the top. Women from every village had come to her house and purred their soft-voiced '*A-ah!*' over the amazing creation of the Mishongnovi woman. The full-length figure of Angwusnasumtaka had been worked in as it had been planned, except that Sikyanömsi had been somewhat nonplused as to how to plan the feet, and had solved her problem by making them both point sideways in the same direction, although the Crow Mother of the gods was shown to be looking straight forward from the basket.

Letaiyo had glowed with pride over his wife's achievement whenever visitors came to her house to admire the famous product of her art; and it was partly as a result of his urging and partly as a result of her own desire that she decided to keep the basket for their family use, and not to part with it for any of the fascinating articles that the trader kept dangling before her covetous eyes.

Two more years passed, and life became focused to a definite reality for small Kwayeshva. The dim figures of his babyhood were resolved into the clear-cut personalities of the members of his family and of their neighbors. The yellow-masked being who had given a rattle to the year-old boy had come to be recognized as the most popular of the Hopi gods, the Kokle Katchina who comes to Mishongnovi every February and gives presents to the children during the great Powamuya ceremony.

The third winter of the small boy's life was a time of great excitement for Kwayeshva, especially on the morning when he had seen the gods, Kokle and others, come along the trail from the eastern ledge of the mesa carrying great bundles of gifts. Kwayeshva had hopped about like an excited sparrow as he and many other youngsters of the village followed these strange masked beings through the streets.

Clack, clack, clack, the children heard the turtle-shells rattle where they were tied to the calves of the legs of the gods who strode briskly past the village houses. Clack, clack, clack, with each step that brought them nearer to the village square where the people were waiting expectantly.

Each pack that the Katchinas carried on their backs was crammed full of exciting, colorful toys. Dolls of all kinds, dozens and dozens of miniature gods as well as drums, bows and arrows, and baskets.

When the Katchinas reached the center of the plaza, they put their bundles down on the ground. As Kokle is one of the few gods who talks before humans, a long dialogue followed in which the leader of the gods was addressed by two old men of the village. Kwayeshva kept running about all through these speeches. He was not in the least interested in the long welcoming addresses of the village fathers, for his mind was full of thoughts of the fun he would have playing with his new toys.

The warm southern sun had penetrated through the icy air of winter as Sikyanömsi and her three daughters sat in front of a relative's house, waiting patiently for the time to come when the presents would be handed out to the children. As they sat there the red and white cloaks of the women made flaming spots of color against the adobe and stone walls of the house. The spirits of the women seemed to be quite as bright as their cloaks as they chattered and laughed in highest glee.

Kwayeshva, who had been running up and down the plaza, all at once stood still as he noticed that one of the Katchinas had, fastened to the pack on his back, a huge painted drum. He stared at it for some minutes in round-eyed fascination. Probably some big boy would get that; but what fun it would be to pound away on that drum. Perhaps the boy who got it would let him play with it sometime.

The last of the Katchinas clacked his way to the center of the village square, and then they all began to distribute the gifts that they had brought from their home at the Shadow Spring to the children of Mishongnovi.

Kwavöhuh was the first of Sikyanömsi's family to receive a present. As one of the Kokle Katchinas handed her a small flat doll made in his own likeness, 'Nömsi, in whose lap the little girl was sitting, called out to him: '*Askwali — askwali.*' Then to little Eagle-Breast-Feather, 'Say *askwali* to that Katchina.' So the little round-faced girl, hugging her doll, looked up at the god and happily but shyly whispered, '*Askwali.*'

'*Wi — ancha'ai,*' responded the Katchina in the high falsetto voice with which the impersonators of the gods always disguise their human tones. Then he turned back to the center of the plaza to secure a fresh supply of presents.

Not long after, Kwayeshva was given a bow and arrow, which gift made the small boy feel that now he was quite grown up. However, in spite of his pleasure in receiving the weapon, more than once he eyed that altogether fascinating drum that still reposed in the middle of the village square. Perhaps Black Bear, the older boy next door, would get it, in which case Kwayeshva surely would be allowed to play with it occasionally.

It happened that the little boy had stopped running about and was standing in a dark passageway playing with his bow when one of the Katchinas picked up the drum and started walking about the plaza. Peering about through the crowds, he searched and searched; finally he passed by the house where 'Nömsi was sitting and the mother made a barely perceptible sign pointing to the shady corner where her son was standing.

Then, as Kwayeshva thrilled with sudden anticipation, the masked god walked up to him and presented him with the drum, which was almost as big as the boy himself. Completely speechless, the child stood looking at his drum while he clutched the stick that had been handed to him.

This drum was his own. He could play on it whenever he wanted to. The small boy's heart was full of happiness and gratitude toward these wonderful gods who were so good to the children. Of course he was quite unaware of the fact that Letaiyo had made the drum and, masked as a Katchina, himself had presented it to Kwayeshva.

When the boy tried to take the drum over to show it to his mother, he found that it was so big that he could just barely drag it along the ground. His grandfather, Makya, came to the rescue.

'*Aie*, Kwayeshva, now maybe you are somebody. You will be *pöhsökinaya*, big Hopi drummer, so maybe Makya will have to teach you many songs.'

The boy grinned happily at the old man and followed him across the plaza and then, radiant with pride, he showed his precious new present to Sikyanömsi. The Hopi woman pretended to be greatly surprised, although she had seen her husband working on the drum for weeks past, carving it out of a section of a huge cottonwood trunk, in the secrecy of a door-bolted outbuilding.

More presents were given to the children, among them bunches of yellowish green bean sprouts which, being presented in midwinter, furnished further convincing proof to the children — if any were needed — that these kindly beings were real gods and endowed with magical powers.

Finally, after a speech of farewell from the village fathers, the gods withdrew and the people scattered to their different homes. When they reached their house, Sikyanömsi told the girls and Kwayeshva to put their beans on a cotton robe which she spread out on the floor.

'Now, maybe,' she suggested, 'you children will go outside and get some wood for our fire.'

So the youngsters rushed out of doors and presently reappeared, each one carrying a stick. Then their eyes grew wide with astonishment, for while they were away, by some amazing miracle, their little bunches of sprouts had grown into a huge green heap.

That afternoon a great many gods danced or marched about the village, but Kwayeshva was so excited over his new drum that he was almost unaware of the stirring ceremonies that were being enacted; for his whole being was vibrating with the sounds that he made as he pounded away on the huge, resonating drum. As he did so, his mother looked at him with intense pride, for the little three-year-old Kwayeshva was trying to sing in the manner of the Hopi men, uttering grunts and vocables with an occasional word thrown in.

That night the family feasted on the slightly bitter bean sprouts. Then, when the bowls and sheepskins had been put away, the children played with their new toys.

Kwayeshva, romping about the room, happened to remember that, in addition to the drum, the Katchinas had given him something else — a bow and arrow. So this seemed to be a good time to play with that as well. As he lifted the shaft of a blunted arrow to the rawhide bowstring, his now full-grown cat, Moosa, stalked across the room right in front of him.

Such a convenient target could not be ignored, so twang! went the bowstring, and a sudden howl of terror from the cat attracted the attention of the boy's parents. As the stricken animal fled to the security of a space behind the piled-up cedar logs, Sikyanömsi looked upward toward the rafters. Then, turning toward Letaiyo, she motioned upward to the dust-covered arrow that at Kwayeshva's birth had been wrapped with a piece of the baby's umbilical cord.

'Some day our boy will be big hunter,' she said proudly.

IV. THE EYES OF SOYOKO THE WITCH

ONE afternoon old Makya stretched himself before the doorway of Sikyanömsi's house while the cooling sun of November poured its remaining warmth over his aged body. He lay there for hours, gazing across the desert, his mind as completely at ease as his motionless form. The dogs that chased the chickens or each other, the burros that hopped determinedly about, no more affected the old man's peace than a falling yellow cottonwood leaf would mar the tranquillity of the motionless desert air.

Above a single thin, tenuous cloud gave of its meager substance in cast-off wisps until there was practically nothing left, and then the last white flake vanished into the enveloping blue.

In Makya's face there was the peace of the desert in repose; its austerity and grimness relaxed by the rare gentleness of the sun's warmth. For fighting resistance there was no need, as the remorseless fire of midsummer had cooled and the frozen blasts of winter not yet come. It was fall, the season of experienced tranquillity, and Makya, whose aged muscles had strained and toiled since early spring, bathed himself in repose in the kindly rays of Tawa, the sun.

He turned his head slightly as 'Nömsi, a water jug slung over her back, hurried out of the door and down the sandy slope to the Toriva trail.

An hour passed, and still the old man lay there while pointed shadows reached out across the town. Then, as they grew to enormous size and blotted out the light, cold air began to filter through the warmth that still clung to the ground. With a sigh of regret, Makya drew himself back from dreams to reality, moved his stiffening legs, and then slowly arose from the dust-powdered doorstep. Just then his daughter-in-law, breathing fast but smiling happily, appeared from behind the sand slope, lugging on her back the earthenware jug of water. Straightening her bent body, she removed the tumpline from her forehead and, leaning over, put the pot just inside the door.

'Yeshva, nude as the day he was born, wandered across the street, unconcernedly grasping his struggling cat by the simple method of maintaining a strangle-hold around its neck. His sister, Eagle-Breast-Feather, came tagging after him, trying ineffectually to pry the cat loose from 'Yeshva's arm. Moosa in the meantime was struggling desperately to do the same thing. But the more the girl and the cat struggled, the tighter 'Yeshva squeezed.

The mother, standing at the door, looked at them for a moment and was about to speak when suddenly she realized that the room behind her was quite dark. Turning quickly, she looked at the hearth and saw only the faintest of embers glowing in a mass of ash. Her face clouded with sudden anger as she spoke sharply to her six-year-old daughter:

'Kwavöhuh! Look at that fire! Didn't I tell you to put stick on it when I went to Toriva? Now you hurry and get cedar bark before our fire goes out.'

Muttering angrily, she hurried to the hearth, and kneeling down began blowing life into the dull-hued coals. Presently the little girl scampered across the floor, clutching a handful of tinder, which she handed to her mother. 'Nömsi sprinkled it over the coals, and then once more blew vigorously. The smoke had just begun to be dotted with sparks when a frantic howl from the cat made the Hopi woman turn quickly around.

'*Aie*, 'Yeshva!' she screamed at him; for her only son, quite calmly and deliberately, was pouring over the writhing, squalling cat the precious water that his mother had just carried from the distant spring. Darting across the room, she wrenched the jug from the boy's hands — which enabled the cat to escape — shook the pot for a moment, and by doing so discovered that it was nearly empty. Angrily she yanked at her son until the usually pampered 'Yeshva howled with fright.

'Now,' the exasperated mother inquired, 'where do we get water for our supper?'

Kwayeshva was far too scared to answer, and his sister's round black eyes reflected the boy's fear. Still angry, but without loss of temper, the mother marched her son over to the hearth and pointed to the gleaming coals that had not yet burst into flame.

''Yeshva, do you see those big fire eyes burning there?' 'Nömsi's voice was vibrant with controlled emotion. 'It is Soyoko whose eyes look at you and see that you have been bad boy. Soon she will come to Mishongnovi, and maybe, if you are bad again, she will take you away to her cave, and then your mother will never see you again.'

In sudden terror at this horrible prospect, Kwayeshva flung himself against the comforting softness of his mother's blue-clad body and sobbed as if Soyoko, the witch, were at that moment standing over him, brandishing her sharp-edged knife. Relenting instantly, the woman looked down at her small, shaking son, then patted his back gently.

'Soyoko does not hurt good children,' she said reassuringly. 'It is only when they are bad and make their mothers unhappy that she punishes them.' Sniffling and gulping, 'Yeshva looked up at his mother while the tears still welled out of his round, black eyes, and made little tracks through the dust that covered his face. Taking him up in her lap, Sikyanömsi continued:

'Hopi people have very little water, and when she needs some your mother must get it from Toriva Spring and carry it on her back up that long trail to Mishongnovi.'

With a final pat, she put the boy down on the floor and then turned to her smallest daughter, who was wiping her nose on the back of her hand.

'And you, Kwavöhuh' — the sternness crept back into the mother's voice — 'you were bad, bad girl, and maybe Soyoko will be mad with you too when she comes in winter.'

However, the little girl's wide-eyed look of fright changed to a smile of anticipation as her mother reached up to the low rafters and, poking her fingers into the dusty thatch, drew out a round, furry object, which, when it had been blown to approximate cleanness, was found to be a bulrush, one of several which had been brought to the children by the Katchinas from their Shadow Spring, Kisiuva, where many of the gods have their home.

Giving a piece of it to each of the children, 'Nömsi then

hunted around until she had found a small pot containing sheep's fat. Then she smeared a generous bit of the greasy substance on a hand of each child. Happily the children chewed bits of bulrush blended with fat, until it became a most effective gum that could be chewed indefinitely. Their faces, a complete mixture of grease, bulrush, dust, and tears, shone in the light of the now sparkling fire, while 'Nömsi, after borrowing water from a neighbor, hurried about preparing the evening meal.

The month of February had brought intense, breath-seizing cold to the land of the mesas. Snow lay on the ground and crunched pleasantly under the soft red moccasins. Late one afternoon the boys were running about, jumping and frisking as they chased a hobbled burro through the narrow streets of the village. As they pursued the frantic animal past Sikyanömsi's house one of the boys let out a startled '*Aie!*' and grabbed at his nearest neighbor.

'Look — Soyoko!' he whispered in a hushed voice.

The other boy followed the direction indicated by the pointing finger; then the whole group turned and ran. For coming up the steep trail into the village was the sinister black figure of the witch. On her head was a coal-black mask with huge, round yellow eyes. A broad, red-rimmed mouth was marked with a zigzag line representing teeth, and from her chin was suspended a small black beard. In her hand she held a long, white crook and on her back was carried a large basket.

She advanced slowly and stopped to knock on the door of Sikyanömsi's house. The woman came to the door, and stood there while her three daughters tried to make themselves invisible behind her fat, matronly figure, while Kwayeshva, being thoroughly scared, clung to the skirt of his mother's blue dress. In a deep sepulchral voice the witch intoned:

'Nö-ö-*ki* — I am here!'

There was a dramatic intensity in the pronouncement that sent shivers up and down the spines of the frightened children. 'Nömsi, on the other hand, answered the witch with perfect calm and self assurance.

'*Ancha'ai* — it is well. And what are you here to do?' she questioned.

The scene that followed had been discussed the day before by Sikyanömsi and the man who was to impersonate the witch. However, to the children there was a heart-chilling reality about the whole performance.

Slowly and deliberately the witch explained that, although they had not seen her, the coals of fire on the hearth had been her eyes keeping watch, so that she had seen how bad the children had been. This statement was made appallingly emphatic by a careful, detailed account of all the childish misdeeds for which their mother had reproved them. The witch scolded the girls for laziness and occasional refusal to grind corn or help their mother with the housework. Then her yellow eyes bored deep into the tear-welling eyes of the tiny boy as she reminded him of his much loved but frequently abused cat.

'Nömsi quickly came to the defense of her child. 'Yes,' she admitted, 'he was bad boy and wasted water that his mother had carried up from Toriva' — nothing was said about the feelings of the cat — 'But maybe,' she said hopefully, 'he will be good boy now.'

Soyoko showed by her answer and her general attitude that she was quite dubious about this. But finally she allowed herself to be convinced that it might be well to give the small offender another chance. So she handed some horsehair to Kwayeshva, whose arm was extended to reach for it, being impelled by his mother's guiding hand.

'Now,' growled Soyoko, 'you must make trap. Then with this trap you must catch something and give me some of that meat you catch. Or else——' The boy trembled as he heard the witch relate all the appalling things that might happen if he failed to give her the prescribed peace-offering.

Muttering and leaning heavily on her crook, the witch passed on to the next house, and then in turn to all the rest of the homes in which there were children too young to be initiated into the secrets of the masked Katchinas.

For three days the village hummed with the activities of amazingly well-behaved children. The boys were too busy trying to catch rabbits or cutting wood for the family use to indulge in their favorite sport of chasing hobbled burros. And the girls found that the arduous task of grinding corn, washing dishes, and sweeping up the refuse-littered floor gave them little opportunity for gossip or laziness.

Kwayeshva, of course, was too small to hunt successfully for any game with which to appease the wrath of Soyoko. So his father, acting for him, caught an infinitely small mouse.

When the first white dawn of the third day revealed the buttes and mesas of the skyline, the boys and girls of the village, with teeth chattering apprehension, looked down from the mesa and saw below a fire that burned briskly and ominously at the black mouth of the witch's cave.

As the gray light became tinged with the yellow hues of second dawn, with mounting excitement the children saw the fearful figure of the witch bending over a flat rock. And then, through the crystal-clear air of early morning, the sound was borne to their ears of Soyoko sharpening a huge steel knife on the sandstone before her. Then, after carefully testing its edge, she gathered up her crook and blanket and started to go toward the village.

Three times she advanced toward Mishongnovi, but retraced her steps from points a quarter, a half, and three quarters of the way along the trail. Having thus represented the first three stages of man along the trail of life, she began her fourth approach to the town. This time she was followed by a large group of hideous monsters. Her husband, Taka Soyoko, was there, and several Natashkas, black-masked creatures with enormous protuberant mouths, made of a split gourd, with serrated teeth that clacked together from time to time with a terrifying sound. Two Massauh Katchinas were there, and this double impersonation of the god of death gave to the group an even more sinister touch than was conveyed by the presence of the monsters. Wehuhuh Katchina, wrapped in a huge rabbit-skin robe, was much less frightening, for it is well known that this god is extremely lazy and, at the slightest opportunity, proceeds to fall asleep.

Prancing about, gesticulating their excitement, a number of Koyemsim or Mudheads followed after the rest. All the boys knew that these grotesque creatures were the primitive ancestors of the Hopi who, at the dawn of creation, had pushed their way up through the damp, wet soil of a dark underground world with the mud adhering to their heads in great lumps. These Mudheads, who are prime favorites with the children, always indicate by their presence that no matter how serious the ceremony may be, there will be some laughter and fun to brighten up at least part of it.

As Sikyanömsi's house was the first in the village, the group of monsters stopped before her door, as Soyoko had done three days before, and again the witch addressed the mother of the four children: '*I-tam ö-ki* — we are here!' in the same bass voice that had startled them all on the previous occasion.

Sikyanömsi, acting her part, greeted the announcement of their arrival with an affected show of surprise. '*Ancha'ai* — it is well; but why have you come?' she asked.

The witch, with a sudden flareup of anger, reminded the Hopi mother of their conversation three days before, and that the children had promised to grind meal or catch game and give these offerings to her as ransom to enable them to escape the consequences of her wrath.

'Oh,' said 'Nömsi, in pretended surprise. 'Perhaps they have forgotten all about it!'

Furiously the witch pounded on the ground with her crook, and in a voice that boomed with anger she declared that if such were the case she would take them away with her and roast them over the fire before her cave. While the children wondered why their mother should have forgotten that they were prepared to make peace-offerings to the witch, Kwamana, the oldest child, came forward with a tray of finely ground meal and the others did likewise.

After much grumbling about the quality of their offerings, Soyoko finally accepted them. Then little 'Yeshva was pushed forward, and almost rigid with fright he held out to the witch his tiny mouse impaled on a sharp-pointed stick. Soyoko took it in her hands and looked at it scornfully.

'It is too small,' she declared, in such a state of high indignation that the small boy quivered with fright. Then Letaiyo, who had been lurking in the background, came forward and finally appeased her wrath with a fair-sized piece of meat; although even then Soyoko vowed that it was not large enough, that someone had 'eaten all around it.'

As the witch moved on to the next house, followed by the grotesque members of her family, Kwayeshva and his sisters trailed along behind; keeping, however, at a sufficiently safe distance from the monsters to enable the children to escape if danger seemed to threaten too ominously.

At this second house a small boy lived who was known all through Mishongnovi by the nickname 'Quivihoya,' because he was always boasting or showing off. His parents had scolded; even the Kikmongwi, the venerable village chief, had become angry over this boy's conceit. Still, for all this reproval, the bad habit persisted. So when the Sosoyoktuh reached his house, the boy was brought up before them and it was an angry, menacing, hooting circle of monsters that surrounded the small, frightened child.

On several occasions Quivihoya had claimed that he could throw a rawhide lariat over a galloping horse. So one of the talkative Mudheads reminded him of this bragging.

'You say you are big man who can rope fast horse. Maybe now you will catch slow Koyemsi.'

Quivihoya stood there in an agony of embarrassment, while the dreaded Nanatashkamuh clacked their enormous beaks and the others hooted and whistled. One of the Koyemsim then handed the small, sturdy boy a lariat and told him to rope one of the Mudheads as they ran past him. Kwayeshva laughed with joyous glee as the prancing masked deities cavorted around the once-boastful Quivihoya, who tried ineffectually to throw his rawhide rope over the head of one of them.

'*Aie*, you are no good,' taunted the Mudhead. 'Maybe we have to stand still.'

Even then the boy, weeping with chagrin, failed to toss the lariat over the exasperating Koyemsi, who with scornful gestures took the rope away from the completely discomfited child. Then the howling, beak-clacking monsters moved on to the next house.

Here lived a small boy named Black Bear who had earned for himself the reputation of being a bully. So as the appalling judges made rasping sounds with saws and an old Spanish sword by scraping them over rocks and on the walls of the houses, one of them stood like an executioner before the wide-eyed Black Bear.

'You are bad boy. You are *kahopi*. You fight too much with little boys — you make them cry and their mothers get mad. Maybe now you will fight someone big; maybe you will fight Taka Soyoko.'

The petrified youngster felt every wiry black hair on his head stand erect as the witch's husband advanced toward him with the pugnacious attitude of a wrestler.

Black Bear shut his eyes and for a moment seemed paralyzed with fright, but the continued jeers and laughter of his playmates maddened him to the point of desperation. Finally he opened his eyes and took one look at his huge, hideous enemy. Then suddenly the village street echoed with shouts of laughter.

'That boy is all right,' called out one old man, while 'Nömsi, giggling, explained to her son:

'See, 'Yeshva? Black Bear bit that Soyok' Taka in his leg.'

Kwayeshva hadn't been able to see very well, but the spectacle of Taka Soyoko hopping about howling was screamingly funny to all the children as well as their elders. Black Bear, now that it was all over, secretly wondered how he had ever summoned up courage to attack the monster. Still, he was grinning broadly as he followed the others from house to house; for as conqueror of Taka Soyoko, his leadership over the other boys was firmly established.

At another house, a girl of ten was instructed to wash dishes for the edification of Soyoko and her family. As the trembling child tried to wash out the greasy interior of a clay pot that had contained stew, her nervousness caused her to drop the bowl on the frozen ground, where it broke into many pieces. Her dismay over this clumsy action upset her so completely that the masked impersonators decided that a touch of humor would relieve the situation. So one of the white-eyed Mudheads picked up the largest fragment of the bowl, and with pantomimic gestures to the others to keep perfectly quiet, he tiptoed over to the adobe oven, against which Wehuhuh was leaning, having taken advantage of the opportunity to go to sleep.

While the other Koyemsim as well as all of the people tittered their anticipated relish, the mischievous Mudhead dropped the piece of pottery so squarely on the head of the slumbering Katchina that, in well-simulated surprise, he jumped to his feet and started lashing about with the black and white pole, emblem of Soyoko, which the lazy god always carries.

Kwayeshva had toddled after his mother and sisters as they followed the monsters through the village, and his shrieks of laughter over the conquest of Taka Soyoko and the discomfiture of the lazy Wehuhuh drove from his mind all the fear that had been inspired by his own previous meeting with Soyoko.

It was in the afternoon that the humorous aspects of the ceremony were developed to reach a climax that was intensely thrilling to the children. All the houses had been visited when Soyoko, and her unprepossessing family suddenly allowed themselves to notice a feathered pole that was standing erect at the entrance to one of the kivas.

The witch rapped on the ground four times, and in response to this signal an old man, the kiva chief, climbed up the ladder from the dark interior and asked the witch what she wanted. In peremptory tones the bass-voiced Soyoko asked the significance of the feathered pole.

'Oh,' said the kiva chief. 'We put that there because in four days we are going to dance.'

'Good,' exclaimed the witch approvingly, and for a moment her voice became almost mild in its tone. Then, however, a sudden thought seemed to strike her.

'Four days.' She let a rasping edge creep back into her voice. 'We can't wait four days to see Hopi men dance.'

She paused and seemed to ponder over this problem. 'I tell you,' at last she announced autocratically, 'you must dance now. Then we can see it.'

'*Kaeh* — no,' the chief retorted. 'We can't dance now, we have no' — he paused and slyly looked about appraisingly at the masked group of monsters — 'belts, silver ——' His voice halted as he enumerated slowly the various precious possessions of the different bogeymen.

'Still,' he suggested, as if it were a brand-new idea, 'your friends here seem to have all those things we need. So maybe they will lend them to us so we can dance now and give you good time.'

The witch expressed violent disapproval of this intimation, but obviously she wanted to see the dance. Observing this, the kiva chief tried to flatter the grim-visaged female, who was stroking her beard reflectively.

'Somebody told us that you are good dancer,' he observed with unctuous diplomacy. 'Maybe you will dance with us and then everybody will be happy to see you.'

Menacing bogey-woman though she was, it was evident that Soyoko was highly susceptible to blandishment. So she persuaded or rather ordered her fellow monsters to part with their treasures, and then followed the kiva chief down the ladder.

As the children chattered in delighted anticipation of the fun that was to come, sounds could be heard from the ceremonial underground room which indicated that Soyoko was practicing with the men of the village. Presently she reappeared climbing up the ladder, followed by the men, who were dressed for a Buffalo dance. Soyoko, however, had been rigged up in such a ludicrous manner that all the people shouted with glee when she appeared. Red, green, and yellow ribbons were festooned from various protruding portions of her anatomy, and imitation flowers were tied to her hideous black mask. Still, while the people shrieked with mirth, it was obvious that the witch was extremely proud of her new finery.

To the children it was a joyous occasion, and when the performance started and Soyoko was shown to be the worst dancer that had ever set foot upon the Mishongnovi plaza, the children hopped up and down with unadulterated joy. First the Buffalo dancers would make a quick turn to the right. Invariably Soyoko would turn to the left and then, recovering herself and finding that she had made a mistake, would take up the prescribed position. Mistakes of this sort are of course screamingly funny, so when Soyoko got her feet twisted all the portly matrons rocked with breath-taking laughter.

It was obvious, though, that Soyoko's mind was not entirely on the dance, for evidently the witch possessed a highly jealous disposition and her husband a roving eye as well as an appreciation of the charms of the Buffalo girls, who had joined the men and were dancing in a line parallel to theirs.

Finally Soyoko's rage boiled over. Rushing to where her husband stood flirting with the girls, the witch hauled him away with her crook.

'You leave those girls alone,' she shrieked with intense anger. 'I am good dancer,' she boasted. 'Come here and watch me. Those girls don't dance right. They are clumsy.' Which obvious calling the kettle black caused all the spectators to laugh joyously.

The henpecked Taka Soyoko meekly followed his wife across the plaza and for a moment watched her dance. His shrewish spouse then proceeded to make more mistakes than ever; while she was recovering from one of these, her husband sneaked away with exaggerated stealth, and had just succeeded in getting near the Buffalo girls when Soyoko, with a snarl of fury, discovered his defection and rushed after him.

In the meantime, the rest of the monsters had been indulging in all sorts of amusing antics. Finally, the stirring rhythm of the dance seemed to arouse primitive, erotic desires in the knob-decorated Mudheads. So, apparently throwing all restraint to the winds, they ran over to the Buffalo girls and became exceedingly familiar.

These amorous actions served as a signal to a masked creature resembling a goat, who thereupon dashed out of his hiding-place in the kiva and charged down on the surprised monsters. As the discomfited bogeymen turned to flee, the men of the village followed the goat and chased Soyoko and her family through the streets, tearing off their backs the cloaks and other garments until nothing was left but an occasional loincloth, and the dress which Soyoko had to retain in order to keep the excited children from discovering that she was impersonated by a man.

All through the day, much food had been given to the monsters. For in addition to the offerings presented by the children, each woman who had taken part in the naming ceremony of a baby was required to pay ransom for her godchild by giving food to the Sosoyoktuh. However, when the rout of the monsters was complete this food was all recovered by the men, and that night a feast was celebrated in every house in the village.

Sikyanömsi placed a steaming bowl of meat before her hungry family as the darkness of night settled over Mishongnovi. Her small son was so weary that he could hardly eat; but it was the happy fatigue of joy that follows fear, of peace that replaces tension. So soon the sheepskins were laid out in a row on the dirt floor, and it was not long before all four of the youngsters were sound asleep.

The fun that had followed the frightening, disciplining ceremonies of the morning had not eradicated the recollection of these harsh measures from the children's minds; for as the winter months passed and spring brought blossoms to the peach trees, Sikyanömsi found that her children were exceedingly well-behaved.

V. EAGLES THAT CLIMB TO THE SUN

THREE more years passed, and the fat, chubby Kwayeshva grew into a firm-muscled boy of six who rode the horses and burros all over the mesa and into the distant fields, who was a leader of other boys in both mischief and in fun, and who spent hours every day beating the drum which the Katchinas had given to him. Singing in a shrill boyish voice the songs that old Makya had taught him, he would sit in front of his house with his huge cottonwood drum tilted forward so that he could reach its upper surface. Then, pounding away, he would sing of the clouds sent by the gods of the four world-quarters; he would tell of their precious cargo which they brought to the 'corn boys' and 'corn girls,' those humanized plants that struggle to grow to maturity in the rippled sand, windblown in the desert fields.

His mother was immensely proud of his singing, and for long periods of time she would sit near him, her fingers automatically binding and weaving the split yucca strands into baskets and plaques, but her mind lifted to the zenith of joy over this amazing man-child, whose second birth had brought him forth from the shadow world surrounding her.

Although he had grown steadily stronger and taller, Sikyanömsi had never for a moment relaxed her efforts to protect and aid her son. With constant care she had participated in preventive rituals that would combat the dangerous evil forces that were ever alert to destroy him; similarly she had acted in every possible way to secure for Kwayeshva the strengthening power of the gods.

Still she did not neglect her three older children, for these girls were being instructed in the making of baskets, in the art of grinding corn to the smoothest fineness, and recently Kwamana, the oldest girl, had learned to make *piki*.

Early in the morning 'Nömsi had built a great blazing fire under the polished *piki* rock. The cedar kindling had spat and sparked as if in combat with some imaginary foe. Smoke, rich with pungent aroma, hung as if it had been festooned from the ceiling.

'Yeshva, who had seen his mother make *piki* so many hundreds of times that he was thoroughly familiar with the process, took a boyish delight in teasing his sister.

'Maybe she is too clumsy!' he shrilled in his boyish treble. 'Maybe she will burn her hand!'

'Nömsi smiled indulgently at her son as she showed Kwamana how to sift the ashes of the *söevi* plant and make a thin batter of these ashes mixed with corn meal and water. All this was very simple, but Kwamana's heart beat uncertainly when the time came to dip her hand into the bowl and rub a thin layer of the mixture over the smoking rock.

Hesitantly she reached toward the thick stone that was black with the smoke from generations of use, while Kwayeshva, snickering loudly, crept across the room to see what was going to happen. Fearfully, the girl dabbed at the *piki* rock so that unconnected spots of batter fell on it.

'*Aie*, 'Mana, you are too slow!' 'Nömsi exclaimed. 'Now you watch.'

While Kwamana watched intently, her mother dipped her palm into the bowl and surely and swiftly passed her moist palm over the stone until she had completely covered a large square. Then, while the children gazed at it with fascinated eyes, the liquid bubbled and dried until it lifted itself free from the rock. Deftly Sikyanömsi peeled it off and laid it on a tray by her side.

'Now, Kwamana, you do it,' she directed.

Once more the young Hopi girl approached the sizzling stone with her batter-moistened hand and then, with her lips pinched together, she rubbed the rock hastily and waited. A thin layer of parchment formed on the black surface. It was not quite square and in the middle there was a hole, but still it was *piki*, and Kwamana had not burned her hand. Smiling with the pleasure of accomplishment, she stripped off the thin sheet and placed it on the tray.

'Maybe now I can make better one,' she declared confidently as Kwayeshva, grinning impudently, picked up the piece of *piki* and stared at his sister through the small hole in the center of the blue paper bread.

All three of the girls helped their mother with the housework as a matter of course, and as the children grew older and their help grew more constructive, Sikyanömsi found that she could give more time to her creative work of making baskets. The Crow-Winged Mother, Angwusnasumtaka, still looked out upon the room from the four sides of the famous storage basket, and during the three years that had passed since her masterpiece had been created, Sikyanömsi had increased her great reputation by making round plaques decorated by designs symbolizing the masks and head-dresses of many of the Katchinas. Siskyap Katchina, great deity of the Corn Clan; Tsoshbushnaka, 'the one having turquoise earrings'; Talavai, 'the god who comes in the morning,' and many others were re-created in baskets, and from time to time the trader who lived in the canyon many miles to the east came to 'Nömsi's house and gave her food, cloth, and sometimes Navajo silver for the baskets and plaques that she had made.

With the passing of each year, the fat, bow-legged grandmother showed increased signs of great age. She still climbed the trail from the far distant Toriva spring, but she would have to stop and rest on the way in order to quiet her pounding heart. And when she reached the house her face would be strangely white in spite of the pigment of her brown skin. Still, as long as she could walk, she would continue carrying heavy jars of water. And then one day, suddenly, she would come to the end of her life trail. Until then there was housework to be attended to, occasionally, wood to be chopped, and always water from the valley to be brought up to the rock-walled town.

One day early in December, Letaiyo and all the men of the village engaged in the wholesale manufacture of prayer plumes — buoyant, downy eagle breast feathers tied with little strings of white native cotton. The people, the houses, even the burros found themselves adorned and sanctified by having these airy symbols fastened to the hair of the men, the rafters of the houses, and the tails of the animals.

Late that afternoon Makya took young 'Yeshva out-of-doors and pointed to the mountain peaks to the west, the Snow-High-Place of the gods. Touching the snow-covered cones of these mountains were many clouds, like great steeds waiting to charge forth into space.

'You see clouds by Növatükyaovi?' he questioned.

'*Wi*,' the boy answered affirmatively.

'Clouds are Katchinas,' the old man informed him. Then, touching the feather fastened to Kwayeshva's black hair: 'Eagle feather like this is cloud.' As he spoke a slight breeze caught the fluffy symbol and lifted it for a moment into the air. 'Like cloud, those eagle feathers take prayers of our people to our great gods.'

Later that night he told the boy more about the sacred significance of the eagle; how that great bird, soaring to tremendous heights, must therefore be in intimate relationship to the sun. So, he said, the Hopi people treasure every eagle feather in order that they may derive divinely sent benefits from the use of these plumes.

'It is hard to find eagles,' Makya declared. 'Each clan has some country where clan people can hunt for eagles. Makya, Reed Clan man, hunts for those eagles at Awatovi' — motioning to the southeast, where the last house of the white man's gods had been destroyed one hundred and fifty years before. 'Maybe sometime this spring Makya will take 'Yeshva to hunt for eagles.'

Sikyanömsi, hearing this, was highly pleased, so she prophesied as she did so often: '*Ancha'ai*, some day

Kwayeshva will be big hunter.' The boy grinned happily at his mother and grandfather. Then, as the winter months passed, Kwayeshva became more and more excited in anticipation of this first great adventure.

Finally one morning the old warrior Makya unhobbled his white burro, and having mounted the small animal called to Kwayeshva that they were about to start off for the eagle hunting-land of the Reed Clan, some fifteen miles to the southeast.

The burro was so small that the old man's feet, dangling without the support of stirrups, almost reached the ground. As they rode on Kwayeshva, sitting on the nethermost portion of the animal, with his arms gripped tightly around his grandfather's waist, kept bombarding him with excited questions, to which the old man grunted monosyllabic answers. Makya, like all elderly Indians, could be extremely talkative or the exact opposite. Whenever he settled down to the business of talking, he kept up a flow of monologue for hours at a time. But if he was occupied with something else, it was quite useless to expect more than the briefest of answers to any question.

However, Kwayeshva was too ecstatically happy to care whether or not his grandfather answered, for he was embarked on a thrilling adventure and had become a hunter — a man among men. So they rode on past the desert cornfields, the boy wriggling with excited glee while the old man whacked at the burro with a short stick, more from force of habit than from any hope of making the animal go faster.

Finally they came over the crest of a sand hill to a strange pinnacle of rock that rose austerely a hundred feet above the surrounding desert. By some freak of erosion this column of successive layers of clay and small boulders had been preserved from the ravages of time. On top of it, looking like a meaningless mass of sticks, was an eagle's nest. For months past Makya had been watching the nest from a near-by hillside in order that he might follow the growth of the young eaglets and capture them when they were old enough to be taken from the nest.

To reach the summit of this pinnacle it was necessary to climb up between two adjacent walls of rock, and the passageway was so narrow that only a small boy could squeeze his way through it. So while his grandfather stood at a point some twenty feet below the top, armed with a curved hunting stick as a weapon in case the parent bird should return, Kwayeshva scampered up the steep rock. Then, twisting his way through the narrow cleft that divided the two parts of the solitary butte, he made his way to the top. There he found two young eaglets squawking their fear of this dangerous intruder. Their mouths being open to register shrieking, indignant protest, the aperture revealed so much of their inner workings that it seemed almost possible to see down their gullets to their tiny, meat-filled stomachs.

Wrapping a cotton cloth around his hand to protect himself from scratches, Kwayeshva seized the eaglets and climbed down to where his grandfather was waiting for him. The old man examined the birds with great pleasure. Then he unwrapped from a sack which he had brought with him two little cradle-boards, miniature reproductions of those used for human babies. The squawking birds were fastened to these boards and then tied to the burro's sides with rope. After that, with the boy joyously sitting on the mule's tail, they rode on to the next hunting-ground.

Some two miles to the east they reached the summit of a mesa, and peering over the edge Makya pointed out to his excited grandson an eagle's nest some twenty feet below the rim. The old man looped a braided rawhide lariat around the boy's thighs and then carefully folded a small blanket over the rope to keep the child from being cut by the buckskin strands. Then, unfastening from his primitive saddle a wooden crook similar to that used by Soyoko in hauling her impressionable husband away from the fascinating Buffalo maidens, Makya told the boy just what to do.

As Kwayeshva was lowered over the sheer cliff, he felt a sudden qualm of panic as he realized that he was dangling over some five hundred feet of sheer space. Far below him there was nothing but a mass of huge, tumbled rocks that in ages past had broken away from the cliff, rocks whose upthrust edges were sharp and jagged.

''Yeshva,' the old man called. 'You are all right?'

'*Wi*,' the boy answered, although his voice was husky with fear. He looked up to see Makya peering over the edge, and just as he did so a small rock, dislodged by the man's foot, came hurtling past the boy. Dodging it, Kwayeshva looked down and followed the rock's course with his eye until it disappeared into space. The boy listened for a second for the sound of its impact with the rocks below, but the distance was too great — there was only silence, broken by the occasional murmuring sound of the wind.

As the rawhide noose in which he sat was lowered with jerking, abrupt motions, the extending rope began to sway outward, and then, catching 'Yeshva unprepared, it sent him crashing into the rocky side of the cliff. In the excitement of this great adventure he had forgotten one of Makya's instructions, but when a second time he was swung toward the rock, the boy held his crook in front of him so that its tip caught the blow and kept his body from being bruised.

Finally he reached the crevice in which the eagles had built their nest. The twigs and stones that lined the nest were littered here and there with bones — bones of smaller birds, or prairie dogs, and there was a rotting portion of a lamb that testified to the eagle's raid on some Hopi flock.

The stench from the putrified carcass almost overpowered the small boy, but holding his breath as best he could he reached down and grasped the single squalling eaglet. He had bundled the bird in thick cotton cloth when all at once a warning cry from Makya and an ominous black shadow that swooped down from the sky seared the boy's heart with a sudden burn of terror. While the old man hauled frantically on the rope Kwayeshva looked upward, and there, not two feet above his face, he saw two great claws armed with curved talons like murderous knives, and then the burning eyes, gleaming with hate, of a huge, full-grown eagle seeking to kill this enemy that had stolen its young. The six-year-old boy, dangling over infinite space, stabbed at the bird with his wooden crook just as the death-dealing talons were about to reach his eyes. Held off for a moment, the bird swung around in a swift, swooping circle and dived again toward the small boy, suspended nearly helpless over the cliff's edge.

Makya, his nerves turned to steel with fear for the boy, pulled with every ounce of strength in his aged arms, while he hoped against hope that the child could defend himself for the few moments that must pass before he could be lifted to safety.

Again and again the eagle swooped, an avenging streak of death striking from the air. And parrying every attack, the boy managed to defend himself with the curved stick until, just as he was being hauled over the ledge, he felt a sudden searing pain as of red-hot iron drawn the entire length of his bare arm as the eagle made one last vicious lunge with its out-thrust claws.

One second after Makya had been able to release his hold on the rope he grabbed for his hunting stick, and in spite of the dimness of his film-covered eyes he threw the weapon with such skill that its sharp, hard edge broke the eagle's neck, so that the bird fell on the rocky ledge, a tumbled mass of twitching feathers.

While the blood spurted from his wound, Kwayeshva with his good arm held up the shrieking eaglet.

'See!' he called. 'I still have Kwahoya.'

'*Lolomai* — good,' the old man responded, while his heart, ever ready to appreciate bravery, glowed with pride in the small boy who had defended himself so ably and yet had not been terrorized into losing his grip on the small captive bird.

Quickly Makya took leaves of native tobacco which he always carried with him and bound them with a rag to the boy's arm. The sudden rush of pain as the pungent leaves were laid over the open wound drained all the blood from Kwayeshva's face. But after the eaglet had been cradled and fastened to the burro's side and the dead parent bird thrown over the animal's back in front of the saddle, the boy forgot his pain with the thrilling realization of the fact that he had won the old man's approval and had conquered a dangerous enemy in his first fight as a Hopi warrior.

That night, when the weary, aching boy returned to his home, his mother glowed with pride over the wounded hero and his three eaglets, although Kwayeshva affected to be supremely indifferent to her words of praise.

Early the next morning, with great ceremony, the bald heads of the eaglets were washed, and in the same manner that marks the naming ceremony of a Hopi baby the screaming birds were sprinkled with meal and named. Then they were chained down to the roof of the house, at a spot sacred as a shrine to these deeply venerated associates of the sun.

VI. WHEN BOYS WOULD BE GODS

TWICE every day Kwayeshva took food and water to the eagles chained on the housetop. His personal pride in the captive birds increased as the pin feathers of the little eaglets lengthened into the brown and white plumes of mature birds. Prisoners they were, but while they ate the meat placed before them, their yellow eyes gleamed with the intensity of their hatred for these humans who had restricted their liberty. The dauntless, untamable arrogance, the undisguised ferocity of the birds sounded an echoing appreciative chord in the small boy; and as he watched them tear savagely at the mutton he had brought, Kwayeshva felt that the eagles were charged with power, definitely superhuman beings brought down from their own realm; that it was only their bodies that were imprisoned, for he felt convinced that their spirits were able to rejoin their fellows and soar into invisibility near the sun.

On a number of other housetops eagles perched in chained captivity, to remain there until, after a winter, spring, and early summer marked by Katchina dances, the gods left for their mountain home to the westward. Kwayeshva knew that after this ceremony each of the birds would be killed by having a powerful thumb pressed firmly against its breast bone. The precious feathers which make prayer efficacious would be sorted into boxes reserved for this purpose, and then the denuded bodies would be buried in the cemetery dedicated to these birds. The ritual would be identical with that marking the interment of human beings, and then the souls of the eagles, being freed, would fly toward the Snow Mountain bearing the prayers of the people who had killed them and an apology for the necessity that compelled them to do so.

As every phase of life was impregnated by the religion of his people, Kwayeshva became more and more conscious of the personalities of the masked gods.

First of all, the majority of them were kind, gift-presenting deities like Kokle. They came in great numbers in the winter ceremony of the Powamuya; then quite frequently during the spring and early summer they would dance in the plaza, sometimes for one day, at other times for two. Frequently on these occasions as many as forty or fifty Katchinas, all alike, would dance and sing in order that the rain might come and the Hopi crops mature for harvest.

One day it occurred to the fertile imagination of Kwayeshva, who had recently become seven years old, that it would be great fun for the boys of his own age to dress up like Katchinas and dance and sing in the plaza. Kwayeshva, of course, being the possessor of a huge drum, would mark the rhythm of the dance, while he led the singing of a juvenile chorus. He suspected that a performance of this sort would not meet with the approval of his parents; so as he enlisted more and more boys to take part in the ceremony, he kept cautioning them not to say anything to the older people.

The matter of assembling costumes was rather difficult. In the first place, of course, it was utterly impossible to secure all the garments and other paraphernalia worn by the Katchinas. So the boys decided that all that was necessary was for them to indicate, with paint or with some characteristic article of apparel, just which Katchina they represented.

So for several days they whispered together, and at one of their conferences it was decided, although with reluctance on the part of some of the boys, to allow the girls to take part and represent some of the sisters of the gods. So costumes were collected for these infants, including the two younger of Kwayeshva's sisters.

One day Sikyanömsi, coming up the trail from the spring, heard the familiar sound of the drumbeat, and then she recognized the childish treble voice of her small son. His solo singing was followed by a piping chorus of young voices, some hesitant, others following their leader with rhythmic precision. Climbing up over a rock to see what was happening, 'Nömsi reached a point just below the corrals at the end of the village, and there in a rock-walled enclosure she saw a chorus of eight children, none of them older than Kwayeshva, singing away while her son pounded vigorously on the drum that still was bigger than the boy. For a moment 'Nömsi watched in silence. Then, ''Yeshva! *Öm hinchaki?* — What are you doing?' she called.

For a moment the boy was startled. 'Just singing,' he answered, while the other children looked uncertainly about.

'Well — all right, but soon you come home for your

dinner,' she declared as she picked up her water pot and continued up the hill, smiling to herself over this boy of hers who was so rapidly becoming a man.

Finally the day arrived, and in the gray light of early morning the youngsters smuggled out of their houses the clothing, beads, and feathers that had been abstracted from their unsuspecting elders. And then the men preparing to go to the fields and the women commencing the housework were startled to hear the sound of a beaten drum, followed by the crisp noise of rattles being shaken, but, in place of the usual deep tones of the singing gods, there came the high, uncertain voices of the children.

Into the village the youngsters came, some of them grinning broadly, others barely whispering the words of their song as the consciousness of what they were doing suddenly made them feel scared. Some of the younger people laughed heartily at the childish antics of the boys and girls, but the older and more conservative ones glowered angrily. One old woman who was the head of one of the women's secret societies shouted to the children, 'Take off those things and go home!' But the youngsters disregarded her angry words and kept on dancing, while their temporarily baffled elders made up their minds about how to stop this sacrilegious performance.

While Kwayeshva struggled to carry the heavy drum, beat out the rhythm of the song, and sing at the same time, a line of a dozen or more boys and girls danced in a grotesque but unconscious parody of a ceremony of the gods. Black Bear, whose courage in biting the husband of the witch Soyoko had earned him a place of leadership among the boys, was dressed in imitation of that most amorous Katchina, Hehea. Around his body the boy had tied an old white sheepskin; on his arms and legs were painted the phallic symbols associated with this deity; and on top of his head was fastened a somewhat dingy pod of red chili.

From time to time the boy stopped dancing long enough to chase after Kwayeshva's small sister, Eagle-Breast-Feather, and in all innocence to make the erotic gestures which frequently mark the performance of the god Hehea. Little Eagle-Breast-Feather had been dressed to represent a Tewa maiden, or Hanomana, her chubby brown face being smeared with vivid green paint, while her hair had been cut unskillfully so that an irregularly shaped bang hung over her forehead.

Quivihoya, 'The Proud Little One' chastised by Soyoko, was arrayed in all the splendor that invariably marks the appearance of Talavai or the 'Early Morning' Katchina. To start with, he had abstracted his mother's red and white cloak, and around his neck he had hung a string of turquoise beads that were the most prized possession of his married sister. He had not dared to hunt for eagle tail feathers although he knew his father had some, so in order to procure a substitute he had caught that gay 'Hehea' of the poultry yard, the big white rooster, and to its eternal humiliation he had pulled out all the poor creature's tail feathers and fastened them into a headdress for his own gorgeous costume.

Another youngster had gathered up bits of old cloth and tied them into balls which he fastened to the wiry black hair on top of his head, so that he became a grotesque impersonator of the weird but fun-producing Koyemsim, the Mudheads.

Kwayeshva had been surprised that the protest with which the older people had greeted their arrival in the plaza had been followed by a period of silent observation. He had noticed the people whispering among themselves, but he had not paid any particular attention to a man who had left one of the houses on the plaza carrying a large bundle. He was not even aware of the fact that this man had climbed down the long ladder leading into the kiva, or secret underground ceremonial room. But if the children had not noted the man's actions, the older people had, and they whispered among themselves with little chuckles of anticipation as the children danced away in the middle of the village square.

Kwayeshva, wearing nothing but a ceremonial kilt, was singing lustily, and the members of his chorus were motioning upward with their arms as they had seen the grown-up singers do in order to summon the rain. The boys were leaping into the air while the girls toddled sedately beside them, when all at once from the kiva ladder there came a low, sinister, ominous growl that froze the tiny dancers to instant immobility. With their hearts pounding in sudden terror they turned to look, and to their horror and complete dismay they saw advancing toward them the most vengeful of all the masked monsters, Tchavaiyo, holding in his hand a gleaming, sharp-edged sword. Slowly this dreaded being strode toward them, his growl becoming more and more heart chilling as his deep bass tones rose to a high-pitched shriek of menace.

For an instant the petrified children cowered there, while their eyes seemed to start from their heads in the extremity of their fear. Then suddenly the drums, rattles, and other paraphernalia were dropped as the children fled to the security of their homes. A moment later the center of the plaza was deserted except for the bogeyman, Tchavaiyo, who stalked about peering through the shaggy horsehair that hung before his goggle eyes. For a short time more the monster prowled about the plaza, then still growling he went back to the kiva and down the ladder.

Not long after this the man who had carried a bundle into the kiva could have been seen climbing out of the underground ceremonial room and returning quite calmly to his home.

This sudden dramatic entrance of the dreaded Tchavaiyo furnished final conclusive proof to Kwayeshva that the gods were omnipresent and fully aware of the daily deeds of every individual. From the time when his mother had told the three-year-old child that the coals of fire gleaming on the hearth were the menacing eyes of Soyoko, the witch, to this final manifestation of the vision of the gods, there had been an ascending sequence of events resulting in the boy's absolute conviction that these hundreds of masked gods that came and went from winter through early summer were the great powers that control the universe and all phases of life.

Still, while this religious belief had its fearful moments, it also occasioned many joyous times for the boy. He thrilled to the dancing of long lines of masked gods when, from dawn to dusk, their feet pounded in a rhythmical, concerted ceremony that must inevitably cause the chief gods of the cardinal points to release the rain-bearing clouds and cause them to pass over the Hopi cornfields.

Then, again, almost every arrival of the Katchinas was followed by, or interspersed with, hilarious scenes in which clowns, representing ancestral shades, staged impromptu plays that were always side-splitting farces. Or else they cavorted about playing absurd games for the entertainment of the people. Kwayeshva always began to laugh the minute the clowns came into the plaza, for in the first place their appearance was so funny. Some of them were painted black and white in alternate stripes, and their heads were surmounted by corn-tassel horns; others the color of yellow earth frolicked about.

Then, too, frequently the Mudheads appeared with them and these representatives of most ancient man always made the people shriek with laughter; although on one occasion a white man, or Bahana, happened to see the fun and for some reason or other his face got very red, and he didn't laugh at all when the Mudheads got excited over some of the most commonplace acts of daily life. Kwayeshva remembered how this man, who was a trader from Winslow, had muttered that it was disgusting and filthy. One of the men of the village who knew the white man's talk translated these remarks for the benefit of the others, and they had all been very much puzzled and tried to figure out what made the white man angry. Someone had met the trader not long after this and asked him what was the matter.

'Humph!' said the man. 'It's the nature of dogs to

run around sniffing like that, but for people——!' He had shrugged his shoulders and walked away.

Still, in spite of the fact that many of the Katchinas made the people laugh so heartily and gave pleasure through their dancing, for many weeks the Hopi boy's heart contracted when he thought of that fearful moment when the menacing, blood-chilling figure of Tchavaiyo had suddenly glowered down upon them from the kiva ladder.

One day Kwayeshva was running around through the village playing shinny with a rag ball and a curved stick. He had been batting the ball through the village streets and had come into the big plaza. There he gave the ball a sudden hard whack which caused it to rise high in the air and then to drop neatly through the sky hole, or entrance to the kiva. For a moment the boy hesitated, wondering what to do, for a mat of *nuhta* reeds was in place by the doorway, which signified that the kiva was closed to the uninitiated. Still, balls were hard to make and this was one that Black Bear had tried to take away from him.

Finally, as no one was around, Kwayeshva ran over to the low wall which supported the roof and which protruded some few feet above the ground. The village was still quiet, so climbing up the few steps to the roof he lay flat down upon the low ledge and peered inside. The deep, dark vault within was absolutely deserted; so, with his heart beating faster and faster as the consciousness of his daring increased, he crept down the huge ladder that extended from the floor high into the air beyond the sky hole.

Of course he had been in the kiva hundreds of times, but never before when those *nuhta* reeds showed it was closed. Kwayeshva remembered only too well how the Soyal Katchina, great chief of the Patki people, had placed his prayer stick in those reeds to close the kiva so that the gods could use it. As he thought of these things he became frightened to be alone in that cold, dark room. He looked around, timorously yet curiously; there was very little to be seen. At one side of the wall a half-finished blanket stretched on a loom showed that one of the older men used the place for a workshop; otherwise the room was quite bare. So Kwayeshva looked about and finally discovered his ragged ball.

Then over at one side of the kiva he discovered another ball much firmer and rounder than his own. It was truly a perfect ball to knock around with a shinny stick. So as his heart beats slowed down to normal and his sense of awe subsided, he started playing shinny with the ball on the kiva floor. Around and around he ran, hitting the ball vigorously and being quite thrilled with the novelty of a new and exciting experience. All at once a hard whack drove his new plaything against the kiva wall with such force that the ball burst open, and as Kwayeshva ran over and picked up the pieces, to his complete amazement he saw that inside the cloth covering there were many seeds. Seeds of all kinds.

For a moment he was completely puzzled. Why should seeds be inside this covered ball? Then suddenly, to his horror, he realized that this simple little ball he had been playing with was one of the round knobs customarily fastened on the heads of the Koyemsim, and he knew full well that although Mudheads may be very amusing creatures, they are also deeply venerated Katchinas and extremely powerful. So it was a thoroughly scared Kwayeshva who wrapped up the ball and put it back where he had found it, and then crept stealthily out of the kiva and back to his home.

VII. THE MIRACLE OF THE LITTLE BEANS

For many days after this experience in the kiva, Kwayeshva was a thoroughly scared boy. It seemed to him that if the Katchinas would send Tchavaiyo to threaten the boys and girls who had danced in imitation of these gods, quite certainly they would visit more severe punishment upon one who entered a closed kiva and desecrated a knob from a Koyemsi mask.

The other boys kept playing their favorite game, lying flat on their backs and kicking over their heads a corncob to which was fastened a piece of rag knotted at the end, so that it could be held between the big toe and its smaller neighbor. As they raced about through the plaza and village streets, shrieking with glee over some of the funny incidents attending this kicking game, such as when a wildly shot corncob hit a burro on the flank and startled him to sudden braying protest, Kwayeshva watched them, but he was too much worried to take active part in their fun.

Sikyanömsi, whose sensitive soul always noted any variation from the normal in her son's actions, decided that he must be sick — quite possibly he might have inhaled the breath of their pregnant neighbor, which would, of course, make him ill. So she reached up to the low ceiling and pulled down a bunch of dried *yupngna* roots. Blowing off a cloud of dust from the plants, she ground them to powder, mixed them with food, and forced her vigorously protesting son to eat them. This remedy, to the mother's surprise, failed to cure her son's ailment, so she looked for something deeper.

One night, as she was coming in lugging a large stick of wood, she heard Kwayeshva talking to his father.

'What do Katchinas do when they get very mad at you?' the boy was asking.

'They whip you hard with *mohu*,' Letaiyo informed him.

The boy knew only too well that this *mohu*, or yucca, had a sharp cutting edge. Still, he was not afraid of pain, and this definite statement relieved him of the worry based on uncertainty.

Days passed, and 'Nömsi no longer worried about her son, for she knew now that her child's ailment was not due to physical trouble. But while Kwayeshva became outwardly the fun-loving leader of the boys, he was turning over and over in his mind the thought of what might happen, for his whole boyhood teaching had been to the effect that certain causes produce certain equally definite results. Still, as the weeks passed, his feeling of relief at escaping punishment was mixed with bewilderment; for the gods must have seen him, and he could not understand why they did not visit their wrath upon him.

One day the boys were sitting on a rocky ledge making marbles out of the ashes produced by burning the silver flakes of a mineral. Some of them were chewing pumpkin seeds and spitting the liquid result into the gray ashes; others made this moistened substance into a thick paste and rolled it into balls, which on baking became much harder than the original transparent material.

All at once, without any preliminary mention of the subject, Kwayeshva turned to his friend Black Bear. 'Maybe Katchinas do not always see bad things boys do.'

The other looked appalled at this suggestion. ''Yeshva, you are *kahopi* to talk like that!'

Nothing daunted by this criticism, Kwayeshva grinned broadly and set about the serious business of baking the small, round marbles.

From that time on, this tiny seed of doubt that had been planted in the boy's mind by the failure of the Katchinas to punish him for his misdeed grew, and was nurtured by observation of many trifling things that combined to weaken his faith in the gods who all through his early childhood had inspired him with such fear or respect. Continually he questioned his parents about the Katchinas and their acts, and the evasive answers of his elders failed to satisfy the boy.

The following year he became old enough to join the men and boys in their daily run at dawn down the trail to Toriva and there, with them, to plunge into the waters of the ancient spring.

Some of the boys dreaded baring their bodies to the winter winds, but 'Yeshva loved it. He gloried in the exhilaration that came after a short, quick dip into the ice-rimmed pool, then the swift race up the steep trail to the village. Sometimes the spring was frozen solid, so on such occasions the men and boys bathed in the snow. They all knew that it would toughen their bodies and strengthen them for all the ordeals of manhood.

Shortly after his ninth annual cycle of life had been reached, Kwayeshva rode out one day across the desert with old Makya. One of their horses had strayed in the direction of Palamootsta.

The fuzzy burro jogged along while the old warrior of the Reed Clan, and his young grandson rode on his bare back.

When they were several miles out from Mishongnovi they stopped to scan the horizon. No horse was to be seen, but fifteen feet in front of them they both saw a huge jack rabbit trying to make himself invisible behind a small *sivapi* bush. Without a word, Makya handed his curved rabbit stick to the boy. Tense with excitement, Kwayeshva took it, raised his arm, and crept slowly, stealthily toward the rabbit. The exact instant that Tavu, the rabbit, sprang from his shelter, the boy threw his sharp-edged weapon, and then there was a twitching gray form, a small cloud of dust, and a beaming young hunter, thrilled by his first kill, who looked up into the approving eyes of the white-haired Makya.

That night Kwayeshva was initiated as a hunter. One of the village elders acted as his sponsor, and, placing the rabbit behind the ceremonially kilted boy, he drew it away from him toward the north, then to the west, the south, and the east.

For four days 'Yeshva was not permitted to eat meat or salt, and then on the final day all the boys and younger men hunted rabbits, and Kwayeshva, in whose honor the hunt was held, was the chief of them all. When they went loping down the trail, their horses' hoofs beating on the rock or scattering cloud-banks of dust, Sikyanömsi stood watching them. After nine years, one of her most earnest prayers for her twice-born son was fulfilled at last.

Kwayeshva was a tall, slim youth, hardened to the ruthlessness of desert heat and cold, when his people, with stoic calm, suffered through the worst winter within the memory of the oldest inhabitant. Sub-zero weather began in early December, and it was the day of Ahöla's coming, in January, that ushered in the big blizzard as well as the ceremonial season of the Katchinas.

The cold, clear sunlight of early January had been followed by a grim, menacing atmosphere as the dark, gray sky crushed down on the Hopi mesas. But the people rejoiced in the prospect of snow, because it would mean that their crops would be protected and moisture stored up for the coming spring.

As the first snowflakes were beginning to fall, Kwayeshva had heard the sound of jingling bells, and had run out-of-doors in great excitement to see the Katchinas come up the trail from their shrines. The wind that swept down from the north with relentless driving power had caught the Katchinas as they emerged from the sandy trail on the leeward side of the mesa, and the great embroidered robe of the Sun God was whipped about by the gale.

With Ahöla, the Sun Father of the Gods, came Aha, the Soyal Katchina, supreme deity of the Patki Clan from the south, and Kokozhori, a tiny spotted chief Katchina of the Corn Clan, who shivered as his nearly nude body was lashed by the storm. With these Katchinas were two Corn Maidens, the Blue Corn and the Yellow Corn Girls. In front of them each of these sisters of the gods carried a plaque surmounted with masses of cotton representing clouds. To keep this from being blown away required the constant use of both hands, and just as the procession of deities reached Sikyanömsi's house, the first one in the village, a sudden gust of wind had torn apart the buckskin thongs which held in place the facial mask worn by one of the Katchina maidens, and, although the man impersonating her had quickly hidden his face in his elbow, Kwayeshva had caught a sudden glimpse of a familiar dark face, the face of one of his uncles. Letaiyo had taken the 'girl' into the house and presumably fastened the mask, for a moment later the Katchina maid rejoined the others and took her place in the procession as if nothing had happened.

Sikyanömsi looked anxiously at her son to see if his quick eyes had detected anything, but the turmoil in the boy's brain was only slightly reflected in his face.

With great dignity the Sun God Ahöla led the way into the house, and there, at the left of the door leading into a dark back room, he made four horizontal lines on a three-foot square painted on the wall with dark red paint. As soon as he had made these marks to ward off evil as had been done in Kwayeshva's babyhood, Ahöla leaned forward and with his great feather-tipped staff he described four circles horizontal to the ground; and then he threw back his head, and the quiet of the room was broken violently by a deep-voiced growl that arose in a swift crescendo to a high-piercing falsetto shriek. Four times in all the Sun God did this, and each time his howl was followed by a prescribed ritual in which the tiny Kokozhori shivered, clapped together two wooden corn symbols which he carried in his hands, and with a high soprano voice cried, '*Ko-ko-zho*-RI!' The Corn Maidens had stood behind the others holding their plaques, but making no sound.

As he followed them first to all the clan houses of the village and then to the remaining homes, Kwayeshva's mind was teeming with amazing, startling thoughts. If that Yellow Corn Maiden had really been his uncle — and he was almost positive that 'she' was — why, then, perhaps the others, even Ahöla himself, might be impersonated by some member of the tribe.

By the time the Father of the Gods had 'built' his house with four lines in each home, the storm had increased until the snow had piled up in drifts in every corner where there was protection from the wind.

That night it was a very quiet Kwayeshva who ate his supper from the bowl on the adobe floor, and this unusual repression did not escape the watchful eyes of Sikyanömsi. So she waited to see if her son would speak to her. Just as he was about to curl up on his sheepskin for the night, he looked at his mother and asked with intense seriousness, 'Was it Lomavantiwa who was that Yellow Corn Maiden?'

'Nömsi pondered a moment before replying; then she said:

'My man-little-one, many things must be learned by each boy when he becomes man. Soon you will know these things. Perhaps when Katchinas come for Bean Dance you will find out what you don't know now. You must not say things to other children, because if you tell what you saw to little boys, then the angry Katchinas will come and whip you. They won't whip you with *mohu* but with *ösö*, and if you are whipped with that cactus, then you will die.'

The next day, while the storm raged on, Kwayeshva, acting on a sudden daring impulse, followed one of the old men as he climbed down the ladder into the kiva. Inside there were many men, and some boys little older than Kwayeshva. They were all busy, and as the Hopi boy looked about him with intense interest and carefully repressed excitement, he saw a large number of pottery bowls each one of which contained moist sand. Then he noticed that one of the old men was busily engaged in poking something into the sand. It was all very mysterious and just a little bit frightening.

As Kwayeshva stood near the foot of the ladder, uncertain what to do next, the old man whom he had followed down into the kiva turned to him and in a friendly way asked, 'Have you planted your beans?'

'No,' answered the boy; and then, in complete bewilderment: 'Beans? I do not know ——'

The old man, who had assumed from the boy's actions that he had been initiated into Hopi ceremonial life, looked sharply at the youngster. And then, putting his hand on the boy's shoulder, he spoke to him with a touch of sternness in his voice.

'You go home,' he ordered. 'Tell your mother what you have seen, and if she says it is all right, she will give you a pot to plant beans in. Then you come back.' As the boy started to climb up the ladder, the old man added, 'You must not tell little boys what you saw in kiva or something very bad will happen.'

When Kwayeshva told his mother that he had been in

the kiva and asked her to give him a pot for beans, she scolded him for his rash action, and then told him what it meant to the Hopi to plant those beans in the kiva in midwinter.

'Each man of the village must plant beans in some big pot in winter every year. Kiva chief must keep his kiva always hot and never let that fire die and his men must keep those beans very wet. Then those beans will grow and be straight and tall and strong, and if they are big in that pot of sand when Katchinas come each day, then, because each man grew those good beans in winter time he will have good corn and beans in his fields when summer comes. If bean plants in kiva don't get water, and someone lets them die, then our Hopi crops in summer will die just like those beans.'

After another warning as to the frightful consequences that would result from telling the young children about these secret matters, Sikyanömsi gave a large pottery bowl to the boy as well as some beans, and told him to go back to the kiva and plant them just as the others were doing.

So Kwayeshva bundled a bowl under his blanket and returned to the old man in the kiva, who showed him just where to go for sand and then how to plant the beans in the moist earth; and then, when the pot was placed in one of the long rows of such utensils that covered a large part of the kiva floor, Kwayeshva surveyed it with a feeling of deep satisfaction. For now he had ceased to be a boy and had taken part in one of the great ceremonies of Hopi manhood.

That night Letaiyo explained to his son the main

facts of the Hopi impersonation of their gods. He told him that in ages past the Katchinas themselves had lived with the people and that it had been a time of great prosperity. Some of the gods, such as Alosaka of the Horn Clan, had married Hopi women, and by fathering their children had become the ancestors of new clans. But ease and comfort had weakened the people and turned them to paths of malice and evil, so that they mistreated their powerful Katchinas and forced them to go away. However, before their departure the gods had given to these Hopi people of ancient days masks made in the likeness of the Katchinas themselves. The people were told that in punishment for their misdeeds life would be made difficult for them, and that from then on they would have to battle for existence in an arid desert land. Still, whenever they should wear the masks of the Katchinas and follow the prescribed ritual, they would have power as Katchinas to bring rain and drive away the evil powers that constantly threaten the Peaceful People.

'So now Hopi man puts on mask, and when he puts on mask he is Katchina. He is no more Hopi man, but real Katchina and can make rain come and make sick people strong and make our corn grow. But Hopi man must do other things. He must make many *pahos* and sometimes he can't eat salt. And before he dance as Katchina, for four days he must not sleep with his wife, because if he does sleep with his wife, then he cannot make that rain come.

'Hopi women must not wear mask, but when boys and girls come in Pachava, then girls wear Katchin' Mana mask and wear their hair long down their backs. Hopi boy mustn't know these things because he is too little and won't know why Hopi men wear those masks. When boy is big boy, then Katchinas come to whip him, and then he can wear mask and be Katchina.'

Kwayeshva was only too familiar with the flogging Katchinas, the Tunguf Katchinam, and their mother Angwusnasumtaka, 'One Having Crow Headdress,' and he realized that within a few days these deities would come to the village.

Letaiyo explained to him that on this occasion it was usual for a member of the father's clan to sponsor the child, but that for 'Yeshva a change would be made and one of the men of the Badger Clan would act as the boy's godfather and lead him into the kiva, where he would be whipped in secret by the floggers. Soon after that, for the first time he would be permitted to see the Katchinas dance at night, without masks.

Four days before the Bean Dance was to be celebrated, as the children were about to fall asleep on their dusty sheepskins, their tired eyes popped wide open with sudden shock as they heard the terrifying sound of a hooting, angry-voiced Katchina rushing about out-of-doors, accompanied by the clamor of bells and rattles. Kwayeshva was told that it was Owangozhrozhro, who is reputed to devour rocks and belongs to the group of Ichivuh or angry Katchinas, who must invariably be propitiated. From time to time, during the early part of the night, similar sounds were heard, and when Kwayeshva asked his father about the meaning of this, he was told that these were not real Katchinas, as the men did not wear masks, but that they ran through the village for the four nights preceding the Bean Dance in order to strengthen the children's belief in the reality of these masked gods.

In every kiva throughout the village the beans were growing into strong, slender plants, yellowish green in color from lack of sunlight, and day and night they were guarded with unceasing care by men elected in each kiva to supervise the successful growth of the plants. The old man in the kiva told Kwayeshva that the withering of one beanstalk or the breaking of its stem would frustrate the entire plan and result in crop failures the following summer; and that on the very rare occasions when this happens the men of the other kivas always descend on the kiva where the tragedy occurs and, masked as Katchinas, flog every one of the kiva members with the utmost severity. For these men are all responsible for the actions of the guardian of the beans since they have elected him to this office, and consequently they, as well as he, must be punished.

For Kwayeshva, the twelve days between the time of bean planting and the fateful moment of his meeting with the masked floggers was a period of continuous thrill. He was enormously proud of his bean plants and of the newly gained privilege of entering the kiva with the men. Still, as the twelfth day approached, he pictured to himself the swordlike yucca with which he was about to be flogged. He was not frightened by the prospect of pain, but he was decidedly apprehensive at the thought of meeting the Tunguf Katchinam; for they had been such sinister figures all through his childhood, and even the knowledge of the fact that they were impersonated by men did not quiet his uneasiness.

VIII. A BOY IS LASHED INTO MANHOOD

TOWARD noon of the fourth day before the initiation ceremony, Kwayeshva, acting on instructions from his mother, took a handful of meal and walked through the village until he arrived at one of the homes on the east side of the main plaza.

As he came to the door, the woman of the house called to him: '*Yungya'ai* — come in.'

The boy entered and asked for her husband, Tangaka — Rainbow — of the Badger Clan.

'He went for wood,' the woman said. 'Soon he will come. You wait here.'

So 'Yeshva sat down, still clutching his handful of meal.

It was obvious to the woman that the boy had come to her house in order to ask her husband to be his ceremonial godfather in the flogging ritual that would take place in four days; also to act in the same capacity some years later in the final initiation into the four great secret societies of the Hopi.

After a few moments a squat, powerfully built man entered the room carrying an armload of wood, which he threw down by the hearth. As he turned, he noticed Kwayeshva, and, as his wife had done, grasped the significance of the clutched handful of meal.

'Yeshva, intensely solemn, through realization of the importance of the rite, handed the meal to the man and said, 'I come to you that you may be my father in those things that are to happen.'

'*Ancha'ai* — it is right,' answered Tangaka and accepted the meal. Whereupon the boy left the house, returning to his home.

Shortly after that the Badger Clan man, whose name, Tangaka, signified that he had been named in his youth by a member of the Cloud Clan, took the meal to a near-by shrine, and with a prayer for the boy that he might be worthy to enter the ceremonial life of the people and endure their hardship with fortitude, he tossed the meal toward the shrine and returned to his home.

Four days later, when the first glow of dawn was bringing light to the village, 'Yeshva arrived at Tangaka's home clad in an embroidered cotton kilt, with an eagle breast feather tied to his hair by a cotton string. Accompanying the older man, Kwayeshva then went to the house of his godfather's mother.

This was one of the oldest houses in the village and was the headquarters of the Badger Clan. Tangaka's mother had prepared a bowl of suds from yucca root; then her sisters and her daughter washed Kwayeshva's head with a perfect ear of corn, put meal on his face, and named him in turn Hovelo, a term describing the white stripe that characterizes the badger; Honansoki, badger claw; Honankuku, describing the paw of a badger, and Honanngamoki, medicine bag of badger skin.

Then, following his godfather Tangaka, the boy walked through the village to the Sun Shrine on the southeastern rim of the mesa. Tossing a pinch of meal to the sun, the older man prayed long and earnestly that Kwayeshva might enter upon this new, steeper trail that was part of his path of life purified of all evil and worthy to learn the secrets of his tribe. And in order that the sun might learn to know him and protect him through the years to come, Tangaka then recited the list of the boy's new names.

While Tangaka was making his silent prayer to Tawa, the Great Father of the Hopi, Kwayeshva did likewise as he clutched in his left hand the perfect ear of corn with which his hair had been washed and which, symbolizing life sustained by food, was called his 'mother.' After he had finished his prayer that he might live a life in which he would be true to the faith of his fathers until in his old age he should fall asleep, Kwayeshva returned to his home, where he was allowed to partake of food that contained no salt.

The great day dawned crisp and cold and a steel-blue sky hung over the snow-covered desert.

All through the village there was intense activity as boys and girls, godfathers and godmothers prepared for the ceremony. To the children it was as if a mist had blotted out the everyday reality of their lives. There was a blank opaqueness of mystery, for many, the darkness of fear; to all of them the menacing figures of the flogging Katchinas were only too familiar. Ever since infancy, year after year they had seen those gods file into the village following their Crow-Winged Mother. They had watched them go into the kiva and then heard the ominous sound of whips in action, followed by an occasional cry of pain muffled by the depths of the underground room.

All through these years they had watched their older brothers go down into the dark mystery of the subterranean kiva. Now their turn had come. So even though the sun shone brightly on the dazzling white snow and the hobbled burros hopped about and the dogs chased each other through the village streets, these commonplace scenes were barely perceptible to the youngsters who soon were to be lashed into maturity.

In Sikyanömsi's house 'Yeshva stood tall and slim, wearing nothing but his embroidered cotton kilt and waiting for his godfather to arrive. The boy grinned at his mother from time to time and affected an air of complete indifference, although his body twitched occasionally as he pictured to himself the deep, dark kiva and the menacing, vicious figures of the monsters who would flog him there in the semi-darkness. The three girls giggled and whispered to each other in high excitement. They had been flogged, and so they knew full well what an ordeal confronted their younger brother.

For 'Nömsi it was a moment of great pride, for her twice-born man-little-one would be a little one no longer. His path through childhood was fading into the background of the past; and now, as a man, he would take his place in the ceremonies that are the active expression of the beliefs and aspirations of the tribe. From the dawn of all time they had come, these mighty Katchinas of the Hopi, and from now on her son, her Kwayeshva, would dance, race, or stand in solemn prayer, masked and wearing the sacred robes of the great beings who dominate and rule the world.

Letaiyo had been asked to act as godfather for the

boastful Quivihoya, 'Yeshva's playmate, so he left the house just a moment before Tangaka arrived, to escort the boy he was sponsoring to the kiva.

The broad red bands on the cloaks of the women and girls flamed vividly against the piled-up snow on the north side of the kiva. The bare bodies of the men and boys rippled with an occasional shiver as they stood on the outer ledge of the ceremonial room waiting for the signal to descend. Watching near-by were Sikyanömsi and her three daughters, as well as many of the village people whose children or relatives were to be initiated.

Suddenly from the distance came a cry, 'They are coming!' and through the clear winter air came the faint sound of turtle-shell rattles. Then, in response to an invitation from within, the long line of children and adults descended the ancient ladder to the floor of the dimly lighted kiva.

As Kwayeshva climbed down the last rungs he noticed that on the part of the floor over which the ladder leaned there was a painting made of different-colored sands, showing the Crow-Winged Mother, Angwusnasumtaka, and her two sons, the Tunguf Katchinam. The figures of these gods had been executed with great realism, and it occurred to the boy that the central figure, that of the mother of the floggers, looked almost exactly like the quadruple reproductions on Sikyanömsi's famous basket. The boy's ever-alert mind for a moment caused curiosity and interest to pierce through the veil of fear as he saw an elaborate altar erected behind the sand painting and, fully masked, two Katchinas whom he had never seen before, one with a green face and the other vaguely visible against the black shadow that bordered the room, a being who seemed to be sucking on something, which later the boy learned was salt.

A whimper of fear from one of the little girls standing near him brought Kwayeshva from his brief exploration of the room back to the consciousness of the ordeal that would test his bravery. For a few moments after their entrance into the kiva, the room was hushed with expectancy. The youngsters were all seated on the low ledge that lined the kiva wall and their small bodies were rigid with apprehension. The girls drew their cloaks about them tightly, as if to shut out the chill that crept into their hearts through the stillness of the stone-walled room. High above them a patch of sunlight shone on the west wall, but below there was only darkness, mystery, and fear.

As in a daze, Kwayeshva was aware of the green-faced god Kalavi, who pressed stone axes against his body to give him fortitude, as years before corn ears had been placed against his infant breast to give him life.

Suddenly from outside a hooting sound was heard, and an instinctive jab of terror thrust itself through Kwayeshva's heart as he recognized the sound always made by the Crow-Winged Mother. Then, following a dialogue between this goddess outside and the kiva chief below, down the creaking ladder came the flogging gods and their hooting parent. Turtle-shell rattles clacked as they descended from rung to rung, and the children edged nearer to each other as the ritualistic dialogue of god and chiefs continued.

The half-hour ceremony that followed was burned intc

the boy's memory with the fire of pain and fright, to remain forever a vivid marker on the trail of life. There had been the Crow-Winged Mother, gorgeous in her embroidered robes and black-winged mask, who had perched on the long, tapering ladder so that no panic-stricken child could possibly escape. All through the whipping ritual this mother of monsters had shrieked to her formidable goggle-eyed sons to whip hard; to lash out all the badness from the children's bodies and under no circumstances to spare them.

There had been the picture of the Tunguf Katchinas themselves, trotting about the rectangular sand painting, brandishing their knife-edged yucca whips. Then child after child was brought forward, pinches of meal given to the gods as an offering and small backs bared to the whip as the young boys, one at a time, stood on the colored sands. Their hands had been held before them by their sponsors, and through the noise of the Crow-Winged Mother's shrieks and hoots had been heard the swishing, sibilant sound of the lash, four times descending on each brown back.

Less vividly Kwayeshva remembered the godmothers who removed the little girls' red and white cloaks and led them forward, some of the children sobbing and hysterical, others shivering but making no sound; one girl so nearly insane with fear that her godmother offered her own body for the whipping, to spare her completely unnerved charge.

Lastly, more flogging as all the men present, and some of the women, with pinches of meal requested the gods to drive out evil of sickness with their *mohu* whips. And then the clacking noise of rattle-decorated deities climbing the ladder, bearing broken yucca spears that bore mute evidence of the power that had been behind those curative lashes.

The Kwayeshva who had entered the kiva as a child emerged as an adult member of the tribe. The four livid welts across his back were the signature of the gods to that effect, and as he walked through the street toward his home, he looked at his younger playmates — still carefree and chasing one of the hobbled burros — and with a sudden sense of shock he realized that with the whipping had come a totally new outlook on life. For fearful and terrifying as the ordeal had been, still it signified the passing from childhood to the age of responsibility; that on him had been bestowed the power to participate in the ceremonies that enable man to direct the might of the Hopi gods — to draw rain from the elusive clouds, to bring up from the sand-encrusted earth the corn and the beans that give life to the cliff-dwelling people.

IX. THE WINTER FEAST OF JOY

THE next morning, when Kwayeshva climbed down the ladder to harvest his bean plants, the gray light of early dawn was just beginning to filter through the hatchway of the kiva. Darkness still clung to the corners of the room, and in the twilight the dimly perceived figures of many men could be seen, each one cutting off, close to the ground, the waxlike, translucent stalks that he had grown.

For the first time in two weeks, the fire had been allowed to burn down to a bed of coals. The stifling, oppressive heat that for so many days had choked the kiva members had passed upward into the night and had been replaced by the cool, crisp air of winter dawn.

Outside, Tawa the Sun pushed his forehead up over the eastern hills, and with the coming of light, joy seemed to spread suddenly through the whole village of Mishongnovi. Like a rising tide it rose higher and higher, stirring the people from sleep and making them tingle with the awareness of the happiness that was in store.

The children awoke, filled with excitement over the thought that their favorite gods were coming with the sun; that they would clack their way into the plaza; that their backs would be bent with the weight of huge bundles of colorful presents.

Two hours earlier, the men had stolen stealthily through the dark carrying the presents which they had made. All these they had piled together at the eastern ledge — dolls, drums, bows, moccasins, and baskets — so that their rich color stood out against the drab background of the rock with the contrasted effectiveness of a rainbow flung against a leaden sky. At one side, a row of yellow masks stood ready to transform serious, earnest Hopi men into falsetto-voiced gods whose coming would bring ecstasy like unshadowed sunlight to the small children of the tribe.

Kwayeshva had cut his bean sprouts with the rest of the men and boys and, with the exception of a few bunches that had been taken to the Katchina ledge, he had given his symbolic greens to his mother, who had hidden them so that no small child who happened to enter her house might see them.

For the boy, the act of participating in this great Bean ceremony had enriched it with a new depth of meaning. Instead of a surface picture painted with broad, brilliant strokes, it had become a living reality, pulsating with life from the ancient past.

The whole joyful, vivid ceremony of the Powamuya had become increasingly familiar to the boy from the time the first Kokle had given a green rattle to the cradled infant, on through the years when other toys, including his beloved drum, had been presented to the growing boy. Now his days of childhood were over. Soon he would be allowed to wear a mask and be a god, dancing with other gods.

As he watched the gift-laden Katchinas march into the plaza, surrounded by children who fell all over each other in their excitement, Kwayeshva thought to himself that for these boys the masked gods were still miraculous beings, wafted through the air from their distant home. Complacently he considered his new manhood. Not only did he know now all about the act of impersonating the ancient deities, but he had helped to grow some of the very bean sprouts which they carried. It all seemed so obvious now that it made him wonder why it was that he had not realized long ago that the Katchinas were impersonated by the various men of the village.

Still, even though he knew that his own father was one of them, it did not lessen in any way his feeling of awe, his consciousness of supernatural power in these kindly gods who came to make the children's black eyes sparkle with joy and their parents' hearts glow with utter content.

''Yeshva, what's wrong with you? Are you sick?' The shrill voice of a twelve-year-old boy thrust itself into his reflections.

'Why do you think I am sick, Comes-with-Rain? I'm not sick.' His voice was completely scornful. 'I just like to think about some things,' he added, with an air of maturity condescending to explain.

'What is it, 'Yeshva?' the smaller boy questioned eagerly. 'Maybe it is something that those Katchinas told you when you were whipped in kiva?'

'What makes you say that?' The older boy was instantly alert, his mind ringing with the warnings of the priests that appalling consequences would follow the revelation of any secret ceremonial acts to the children.

Comes-with-Rain was surprised at the note of anger in his friend's voice. 'Oh, I just wonder sometimes,' he said, almost apologetically.

'Huh!' retorted 'Yeshva. 'You are *kahopi*. Maybe

next year you will get flogged and then you will learn something. Now you must not talk, and you must never ask big boys questions like that.'

Comes-with-Rain was distinctly annoyed by this attitude of elder superiority. 'Maybe now you are *quivihoya* — too proud to talk to your friends.' Then, with a sudden change of attitude: 'What is it, 'Yeshva? What is it you learn?' He grinned.

Then, greatly daring, he put into words a thought that had been slowly germinating in his own adolescent mind:

'Maybe you learn that Katchinas don't come from Növatükyaovi. Maybe you find out that Katchinas are just ——' As he hesitated, the two youngsters suddenly became aware of the fact that one of the Kökelom stood beside them with a toy for Comes-with-Rain. His pleasure in the gift turned the boy's thoughts to safer channels.

So, taking advantage of the chance to escape, Kwayeshva walked across the plaza to where his mother was sitting, and as he walked his mind was exceedingly uneasy. He had never asked the older boys questions like this, and it didn't seem fair that just because he had been whipped, those little boys should try to make him tell about things they were too young to understand.

However, the gaily colored scene, the laughter of the children, and the broad smiles of their elders soon banished these thoughts from the boy's mind; and it was not long before he was eagerly examining the toys and arrows given to his younger friends and testing his skill by using the broad flank of a worried burro as a target.

After the Katchinas had retired to their ledge, Kwayeshva became an amused spectator of the simple trick whereby small bunches of bean sprouts, by seeming magic, were made to increase to great heaps of succulent greens.

He had wandered into his aunt's house on the plaza just as she was instructing her small daughter to run out to the woodpile for small sticks. While the child was out of the room, the mother had unwrapped the bundles of bean sprouts that had been brought in secretly by the men of her family, and had piled the yellow-green stalks on top of the small bunch that the Katchinas had given to her child.

Kwayeshva thought it was all a huge joke and that his small cousin was silly to be fooled so easily; yet, a year ago, he had accepted the amazing multiplication quite as unquestioningly as the uninitiated children still did.

In the afternoon, when the people were gorged from the feast of beans, the hilarity of the Powamuya ceremony reached its height, for from each of the kivas in the village at different times a group of Katchinas emerged.

Sikyanömsi and her four children had just entered the passageway leading to the plaza when a deep-throated growl made them look back. Up the ladder that led out of the kiva and in front of their house came Tchaivayo, the same bogeyman who had scared Kwayeshva and his friends so effectively when they had presumed to dance in imitation of the gods.

For a moment the hideous monster paused as he stood on one of the upper rungs of the ladder and peered about, apparently finding it difficult to see, as his goggle eyes were covered with a mat of straggling hair; then he growled so that his voice rose from a deep bass to a shrill, sharp tone that made the few children standing near catch their breath with sudden terror. But their fear instantly changed to laughter when Tchaivayo stepped out on the kiva roof and then down to the ground; for to their intense delight they saw that two intrepid little Mudheads had actually lassoed the bogeyman and were holding him with a tight rein.

As he felt the sudden check of the lariat, Tchaivayo growled horribly, and turning, charged on the tiny little Koyemsim. Instantly they dropped to the ground and held up before them a pair of buzzard-wing feathers to appease the monster's wrath. The magic of the feathers was at once effective, for at the exact moment he saw them Tchaivayo's anger subsided; so, turning, he stalked angrily about through the village, dragging the two little Mudheads behind him at the end of their buckskin rope.

'What is it makes those *wisoko* feathers stop Tchaivayo when he is mad?' Kwayeshva asked.

Sikyanömsi shook her head; then, as old Makya came around the corner, she motioned toward him. 'Maybe your grandfather can tell you,' she suggested. So the boy stopped the old man while Sikyanömsi and the girls walked on farther.

Old Makya smiled when the question was put to him, for anything that had to do with Hopi ceremonial life was very dear to his heart. He squatted down on a cedar log and spat two or three times before he spoke.

Finally, 'You know Tchua, that snake with rattles on his tail,' he said, more as a statement than a question. 'Well, when that Tchua gets mad, he coils himself so he can jump at somebody and bite; but if Hopi man has those *wisoko* feathers and can stroke that snake softly with those feathers' — the old man paused and chuckled with delight — 'it makes him unwind himself so that he can't jump and it makes him quiet so that this Hopi man can catch him. That is how those buzzard feathers make that angry Tchua stop when he is mad. Tchaivayo is like that Tchua; he always likes to get mad, but when he sees those feathers, he knows he must be good, so he can't be mad any more.'

While they still sat on the log, from another kiva a line of Angak'tchinas, long-haired gods with green faces, marched past on their way to the plaza. With them were two of the Kökelom who had given out presents in the morning. Helping himself with his stick, Makya arose.

'Come,' he said to the boy. 'Those Katchinas will dance in the plaza and they will make all our people happy. We shall go see them.'

As they started to walk toward the plaza, they stopped to make way for the lassoed Tchaivayo, who was still roaming around through the village streets. A crowd of small boys followed the monster and the Mudheads. They were obviously held in check by the Koyemsim; some of the more daring youngsters sneaked up until they were quite close to Tchaivayo. The minute he saw them the ferocious deity glowered for a moment, roared with anger, and tugged determinedly at his leather leash while the boys scampered off, their bravery blown away by the storm of the monster's anger.

In the plaza the other Katchinas were dancing in a straight line. They sang their prayers for the health and prosperity of the people as they danced in rhythm for rain. On all sides of the village square, men, women, and children leaned against the houses or sat on the stone steps before them, their gaily colored blankets making the scene brilliantly shot with color. The winter winds swirled and whistled, and occasionally a bit of snow was dislodged from some roof and blown through the sunlit air.

Finally, at the end of the dance, a ripple of anticipated pleasure swept over the crowd. A few laughs were heard, while the gaze of all was directed toward a kiva in one corner of the plaza, out of which more Katchinas were emerging. This time there were but two of them, but their arrival was greeted with shouts of joyous appreciation from the people.

Their masks were white, decorated by a red chevron on each, which had its upper point on the bridge of a protuberant nose. Their bodies were daubed with white clay, while about their loins they each wore as kilt a *chirro*, or small black-and-white checked blanket such as is presented to every male child.

Kwayeshva giggled with high glee as these fun-makers came into sight. As they climbed down the kiva roof, the two Ho-eh started to chatter with great excitement. They appeared to be furiously angry with each other. Each was accused of being lazy.

'Well,' charged one, speaking in a high, falsetto voice to disguise his normal tones, 'if I hadn't waited for you while you chased after those pretty girls on our way, we shouldn't have been so late getting here.'

'While you waited for me!' retorted the other. 'You were asleep, and I had to rub snow on your face to wake you up.'

As they quarreled, they gesticulated with zigzag, flat

sticks representing lightning, which each of them carried in his hand. These symbols, signifying male sexual power, seemed appropriate for these deities, as all their conversation seemed to be of a distinctly erotic nature. They boasted of their past conquests, and discussed with great frankness their plans for the future. Men, women, and even the children shrieked with laughter over the intimate details that were revealed. When the fun had reached a climax, the two Ho-eh then began to dance with great vigor while they chanted the words of a song.

Kwayeshva, wrapped in a striped blanket which old Makya had made for him the winter before, was laughing as gaily as the rest when he heard his mother exclaim:

'See, 'Yeshva! Our Tewa friends from Hano have come to see our dance.'

The boy looked up and saw a heavy-set but finely featured Indian walking across the plaza toward them, followed by his wife, son, and daughter.

The Tewa mother, Pongkwiyo — Snow-Woman — was a tiny little person who looked like a bright, animated bird. Her voice was high-pitched and chirping, and her eyes were black ovals that sparkled like the sunshine on dark pools.

Her son, Mahle, was a tall, handsome youth with a languid expression that contrasted with his obvious strength. After them came the boy's sister, little Butterfly Girl, her black hair standing out in two great wheels from her head. Even the winter winds could not disarrange this *nasumta* head-dress, the squash-blossom symbol of her youth and purity. She hurried along after her parents and brother, her slim little body wrapped in a white cloak with flaming red bands. She was quite obviously excited over this visit to Mishongnovi, for in all her twelve years she had never before visited that middle mesa town. Her dark eyes glowed with interest in the scene before her, but as her family, with exclamations of pleasure, touched the hands of Sikyanömsi and her children, the mobility of the girl's face became stilled by sudden shyness.

As the visitors from Hano sat down beside their Mishongnovi friend, there was a pause between the dances. The two Ho-eh had gone to another part of the town, Tchaivayo could just barely be seen stalking about in the distance, while the song of the singing Katchinas could be heard from the small plaza near Sikyanömsi's house.

During this quiet interlude, Kwayeshva talked with young Mahle, whom he had met several times before. They spoke of their sheep; then, lapsing into boyishness, they laughed together over some of the pranks and games that had recently made life zestful for them both. While they chatted away, Butterfly Girl looked about her, and from time to time little ripples of interest brought animation to the shy calm of her face. Finally Kwayeshva turned to her.

'Maybe you have Katchinas like these in Hano?' he suggested.

'*Wi*,' Butterfly Girl answered. She parted her lips for a moment as she started to amplify this simple response, but a sudden wave of shyness overcame the impulse, so she just smiled at the Mishongnovi boy, a nervous but appealing smile that came into being swiftly and as quickly disappeared.

'Yes, we have Katchinas like these in Hano,' Mahle

answered for her; 'but we have other kinds that you Hopi people don't know.'

For some minutes the two boys talked about the difference in the ceremonies of their two villages. Then Kwayeshva happened to notice little Butterfly Girl. She was looking about over the plaza at the people and their houses with such eager, excited interest that 'Yeshva watched her for a long moment without speaking. The thought of girls as being creatures in any way different from his sisters had never occurred to him before, so it was a new and utterly surprising impulse that made the boy speak to the girl and say:

'Perhaps some day I shall come to Hano and see those Tewa Katchinas.'

A swift look of pleasure for an instant leaped into the girl's eyes. This was a nice Hopi boy, and it would be fun to show him those Katchinas that her ancestors had brought from the great river to the east.

Just then a sudden shout from the crowd caught their attention. Into the plaza they saw coming a fourth group of masked gods; one of them, representing a hummingbird, darted about, his arms outstretched, while he ran with short, quick steps, gliding over the ground as if in flight through the air. In front of his brilliantly colored mask was fastened a long, tapering bill. A huge ruff of black eagle feathers was about his neck. On top of his mask, gaily colored parrot and macaw plumes, treasured rarities traded by Indians from the south, were tied so that their feathered tips projected behind his head. As this Katchina appeared, Kwayeshva exclaimed to Butterfly Girl:

'This is Totcha. He is great fighter, so he had that *hurungkwa* on top of his head.'

The girl smiled happily. She was perfectly familiar with Totcha, who appeared every spring in the racing ceremony at the eastern mesa on which she lived. Then, as a startlingly different Katchina appeared, she overcame her shyness enough to ask: 'What Katchina is that? I never saw that one before.'

'That is Kwikwilyaka,' Kwayeshva informed her. 'He is funny. He imitates everything anybody does. You watch him, Butterfly Girl. I'll make him do something.'

As Kwayeshva spoke, the Katchina walked toward them from the center of the plaza. He was a black creature, wearing dingy clothes. White stripes were on the face of his mask, and rolls of frayed cedar bark were fastened to its top. Darting over to a place in front of the Katchina, the boy began to dance. Instantly the Katchina did likewise, copying every gesture, every footstep. Then the youngster began to run and to jump, in all of which actions the Katchina followed him. Finally 'Yeshva, seeing one of the gray burros amble unconcernedly into the center of the plaza, skipped about behind and finally under the startled animal. The imitator tried his best to repeat these actions, but this was too much for the dismayed burro, who wheeled about in sudden fright, which caused the masked Katchina to run squarely into it. Registering its protest by a vociferous bray, the hobbled animal hopped clumsily away, while Kwayeshva, enjoying the shrieks of laughter from the crowd, rejoined his family and their friends.

When he sat down again by Butterfly Girl, he was flushed and a trifle breathless.

She looked up at him with a smile of thanks. 'I know now what that Katchina is,' she said, rather proudly. 'We have one who does those funny things, but we call him Lapöktuh. Sometimes we have one with many colors.'

'Yeshva nodded. 'I saw one of those colored ones last year in Shongopavi. But you wait, Butterfly Girl; maybe you will see that Kwikwilyaka do something very funny before he goes home.'

Other Katchinas, including the tall and stately Talavai, or morning god, stalked majestically before them. As he looked at the resplendent Katchina, 'Yeshva began to laugh.

Butterfly Girl looked up inquiringly. 'What is funny?' she asked.

Still chuckling, 'Yeshva said: 'That Katchina made me think of something funny that happened when I was still small boy. We all thought it would be fun to have dance like Katchinas, and one little boy we call Quivihoya dressed up like that Talavai Katchina. He got his mother's *atoeh* for cloak, some necklaces that belonged to his sister, and then he pulled out all those tail feathers from some white *kowako*. We were dancing when that Tchaivayo came. He scared us so we all ran away.'

A sudden idea came to him. 'I wonder,' he mused, 'what made that Tchaivayo come. Maybe my father, Letaiyo, will tell me.'

The sun was dropping down toward the snow mountain of the gods when one of the kiva members in charge of the ceremony ran over to where the imitator was walking about. In his hand the man carried a flaming brand.

With a swift motion he raised the torch until its fire just barely singed his own black hair. Then he handed the torch to Kwikwilyaka, while the people all waited with eager anticipation for the exciting event that was about to take place.

The imitator accepted the torch and raised it to his own 'hair' of highly inflammable cedar bark. At once it blazed up, crackling and spitting until the flames from the burning head-dress were leaping into the twilight air. Across the plaza, out through the narrow street, to the privacy of the concealed ledge the Katchina rushed, while the people became almost hysterical with joyous laughter. One of the spectators, an exceedingly fat woman, had been leaning against a low pile of logs. With a sudden exclamation of delight over the Katchina's amusing actions, she threw up her hands, lost her balance completely, and fell backwards across the wooden poles so that her fat, buckskin-wrapped legs were thrust skyward in full view of all the laughing spectators.

Tawa the Sun glided behind the sacred mountains toward the west, and the chill, cold air of night swept through the plaza as the priests who were acting as fathers to the Katchinas made their solemn speeches of thanks to the gods for coming to Mishongnovi and for bringing so much pleasure to the people. One after another the men, women, and older children came forward, and murmuring a prayer thrust sacred meal and prayer plumes into the hands of the waiting deities. And as the tinkling bells and clacking turtle-shell rattles of the retreating Katchinas died away into the quiet calm of advancing night, the people all flocked back to their homes.

The joy that had colored all the ceremonies of the day lingered on as the different families squatted about clay bowls that were heaped high with boiled bean sprouts and other foods. At Sikyanömsi's house, the Tewa guests munched away happily while they chattered with their Mishongnovi friends about all the events of the day. That dramatic exit of Kwikwilyaka in particular had excited them. Food bowls were put away, corn-husk cigarettes were rolled and smoked, while the men and their families sat near the hearth.

Slowly the darkness closed in on the high and rock-bound village of Mishongnovi. Increasingly the air became colder as the night wind swept down from the north. But light sparkled in the Hopi windows as the flames from the cedar fires leaped upward through the adobe chimneys and laughter was tossed back and forth from house to house through the town. The joy that had colored all the ceremonies of the day could not be banished by mere darkness or cold. It was a time for triumphant feasting. The tiny bean plants that were now being eaten had been grown successfully in the kivas, and an abundant harvest later on was thereby ensured. To be sure, they would still have to dance frequently for rain, but the perpetual menace of drought had for the moment been pushed into the background and the hearts of the Hopi were glowing with happiness. Their thoughts were buoyant with hope and confidence as they feasted, talked, and sang.

X. THE GODS DANCE LIKE A FLOWING SEA

AFTER the evening meal was finished and the bowls were put away, the Mishongnovi family and their Tewa guests sat about the cedar fire that crackled and spat merrily on the hearth. Conversation thrust itself occasionally into the semi-silence, but for the greater part of the time there was quiet as they reflected on the doings of the day.

Outside, a rising full moon was poised over the Antelope Mesa, and its beams, like luminous arrows, were shot into the star-sparkling sky and the snow-coated earth.

From time to time the sound of hurrying footsteps was heard crunching the brittle snow outside Sikyanömsi's door and then diminishing into silence, that in turn was interrupted by the nervous yelping of packs of dogs that swarmed about the moonlit streets.

Butterfly Girl leaned back against the wall, and idly her dark eyes journeyed through the room. They explored the prayer sticks, herbs, and Kwayeshva's arrow that protruded from the dust-covered thatch of the ceiling; then her gaze crept down the walls, over the striped blankets that hung on beam ends, until they reached the floor. A gleam of excitement shot into the girl's roving eyes as she saw the crow-winged figure of Angwusnasumtaka designed on a huge storage basket. Excitedly she nudged her father, who was half asleep beside her, and pointed to the corner where the basket was partly hidden by odds and ends of cloth and leather.

Polakka stirred himself from his drowsy state and followed with his eyes the direction of his daughter's pointing hand.

'*Aie*,' he chuckled. 'Now maybe you will see something.' Grinning broadly he turned to 'Nömsi. 'Polimana has heard Tewa women talk about big basket you made. Now she is happy because she sees it.'

Sikyanömsi beamed with pleasure, arose stiffly, and beckoned to Polimana. 'Come,' she said, 'I will show you my basket.'

As the Hopi woman and the slim child from Tewa crossed the room, 'Yeshva jumped to his feet and followed them. Carefully 'Nömsi explained the significance of the symbolism, and as she did so her son grinned happily to see that this pretty Tewa girl was so much excited over his mother's work. This feeling of pleasure lingered on as he watched Sikyanömsi show her little guest just how the plaques and baskets were made. Some unfinished specimens served to illustrate the method of binding the bunched *sohuh* or wild hay with split, dyed strands of yucca. Then to Polimana's joy the Mishongnovi woman presented her with a plaque on which was shown the terraced head-dress and mask of a Hopi Shalako, that great god of the Patki people who dances in the newly built houses of the Hopi.

The child's eyes were glowing with joy when she sat down again by the fire and held her new treasure tightly against her dark blue dress. These Mishongnovi people were such nice friends, she decided, and never before in all her twelve years of life had she enjoyed herself quite so much.

The blue-centered flame writhed about the last crumbling cedar log and then withdrew into the copper-colored coals that were bordered with gray-speckled ash on the adobe hearth. Letaiyo, crouching before it, gazed for a while at the dulling embers with the intentness of a pondering philosopher; then he arose quickly, stepped over the outstretched legs of his guests, and for a brief moment disappeared out-of-doors. As he reopened the door and carried in a thick cedar log, a scrawny yellow dog, scared yet daring, slipped between the Hopi man's legs and darted into the warm room.

When the log was thrown on the blackening coals, little clouds of steam swirled upward as the adhering bits of snow melted suddenly. Outside there was an almost continuous sound of people passing the house, for nearly every man in the village was busily preparing his costume for the final great ceremony of the Bean Dance. At midnight the Powamuya Katchinas would appear in each of the kivas, and on this occasion the boys and girls who had been whipped by the Tunguf Katchinam would see these Hopi gods dance without wearing any masks.

After they had been sitting about the room for some time, old Makya poked his head in through the door, noticed the Tewa guests, hurried across the room to greet them, and then as quickly withdrew, followed by Letaiyo. The cold air from the twice-opened door drove the others nearer to the fire.

For a time they sat there in silence, broken only by the barely audible snoring of the aged grandmother, who lay on the floor, her back against the wall. While Sikyanömsi's mother still tottered about helping with the housework and occasionally carried water from Toriva, she spent a great part of the time in sleep. Almost invariably, when she sat down to rest, her head would begin to slip forward, and then her breathing would become more and more audible until occasionally a sudden snort woke her up and caused her to look inquiringly about the room.

Late in the preceding fall, 'Yeshva had seen his grandmother making her slow laborious way up the trail, while she carried her accustomed burden of water. He had watched the old woman as she leaned against a rock, too weary even to remove the headstrap that held the water jug on her back. A jutting rock had taken some of the weight of the jug, and then the boy had seen Sowüchti's fat old body slip sideways as drowsiness crept over her.

As the trail was steep, 'Yeshva had felt a sudden fear that his grandmother might fall over the rocky ledge, and started toward her, when he saw her head drop lower and lower to one side until the change of position caused a sudden trickle of water to run down the back of her neck; for the corn-stopper was loose. Snorting in surprise, the Hopi woman straightened up and became aware of her grinning grandson standing before her. Indignantly she accused him:

"'Yeshva! You are *kahopi!* You pour water on your grandmother.'

Still laughing, Kwayeshva had denied the charge and then explained to her how it happened that her dress had become wet. Only half convinced, the old woman had told the boy that he was bad anyway and would therefore have to carry her water jug up to the village. Somewhat reluctantly, for that was woman's work, Kwayeshva had taken the pot, and carrying it on his back had trotted swiftly up the steep slope of the trail.

Since then, the deep snow and intense cold had kept Sowüchti at home to work and to sleep, quietly content in knowing that soon she would pass to the skeleton world below.

While Sikyanömsi, her family, and her friends still sat before the blazing fire, the family dog, who had crept into the house when the men left, prowled about looking for food. As he poked about with his nose, he came near to the corner where the old woman lay asleep. His nostrils quivered as he sniffed; then, becoming aware of the fact that some of the grease from the stew the grandmother had eaten was still adhering to her face, he began to lick it off. Instantly coming to life, the indignant woman beat at the dog with her fat, wrinkled fist and then grunted her disapproval of the laughter which convulsed the others.

Outside there was the complete stillness of desert night, broken occasionally by the scarcely audible sound of the men practicing their songs in the depths of the ceremonial rooms. It was Polakka, their guest, who broke the silence in the warm room inside.

''Yeshva,' he said to the boy, 'did you ever hear that story of how our Tewa people came to Hopi?'

'I heard some of it,' the boy answered, 'but maybe you will tell it all to us.'

Few Hopi men need much encouragement when it comes to story-telling, so Polakka spat into the fire and then began:

'*Haliksai* — so it was long ago in Tsañwadi when our people were living there way beyond those mountains' — he waved eastward — 'there our Tewa people lived in many villages; some by big river, some near high mountains where rising sun comes up. Then those white men, those Castile, came on horseback, and with them came men with long dresses. They built big kivas for their gods. In these big kivas they had pretty pictures, and figure of their Castile god, tied on two sticks that pointed to north, south, east, and west.

'It was all right. We had many Katchinas and maybe those white men's Katchina was good, too. We said *ancha'ai*, that maybe this new god would help us bring some rain. Still, when we have our dances, these Castile people all get mad. They say we must not let our old Katchinas dance. They tell us that if we do these things we shall be put in some big fire and all get burned and die. They made us scared, but still those Katchinas are our gods, since long ago our people made their dances with those gods our fathers knew. So it is not right that we should stop. Our Katchinas would get mad and punish us with drought.

'So all our people talk together — Tewa men, and those from other villages — and they say that we must fight those people who will not let us dance. One man whose name was Popeh gave signals to all our tribes. Men ran everywhere. They even came to Hopi and talked to people here. So one day Indians all got mad and fought Castile men. They burned down kivas of white man's god. They killed those angry ones with long dresses, those who always scolded us about our ancient gods. Then many winters and summers passed before Castile tried to come back again.

'Now during all those years our Indian people were scared because they were afraid that Castile would come back again and maybe kill them all. Then one day those white men came. They rode on horses, and some men wore hard clothes made of silver like our bracelets. They were so many that we knew we could not fight. So they came up to our villages, scolded us, and all of them were mad. But still, they did not kill us as we thought that they would do, but just as before, their priests who wore their dresses long told us we should all be burned if we made our Katchinas dance.

'One day some Hopi man from Walpi, Snake Chief, came to Tsañwadi. He told us that people in Hopi towns were having such bad time; that Utseh men made war on them and that Snake Chief's people all were much afraid. So this man said that maybe our Tewa people would come to Hopi and help those men to fight. If we would come, they would give us fields of corn and some fine place where we could build our town. But we said "No, we will not go to Hopi. Our home is in Tsañwadi, and there we want to stay."

'But three times that Hopi Snake Chief sent this messenger to us. Four times he came. Then when he came four times, our people thought that maybe it was right that they should go to Hopi and help to fight those Utseh who want to kill. Perhaps if our people lived in Hopi they could make their Katchinas dance and there would be no men in long dresses to be angry and make them stop.

'So our chief said, "*Wi — ancha'ai*," we would go to

that Hopi land. So that Snake Chief's man said that when we came there those Hopi men would give to us some fine place where we could make our homes on top of their own mesa. They also said they would give to us those fields for corn they promised.

'So our people left their own town of Tsañwadi. They went across that big river that was near. They went for many days across high mountains. It was hard for people to travel so far, and when they came to Walpi they were tired. But still they were happy to find this land where they could build new houses and make new Tewa town.

'But when our Tewa people came to Hopi, all those Utseh men had gone back home and those Walpi were not scared. So Snake Chief then got mad at us. He said that no, we could not live on mesa. They made us live far down below, on some little, yellow hill. They gave to us no fields at all. We had no corn to eat. So our women went to Walpi and said that their babies died. They had no food to feed them. Then they asked those Walpi to give them bread, and maybe some little meat. But those Walpi women laughed and said, why should they give bread and maybe some little meat to Tewa people?

'Tewa chief got very mad. He wanted to go home, but he knew it was too far to go — much too far when they had no food. They could not make this journey. So they had to stay in Hopi, stay and maybe die.

'One day some man ran into Walpi village. He had run from far away, and he told those Walpi chiefs that Utseh had come back and they had many fighters and maybe they would kill all those Walpi people. So that Walpi chief came down to our yellow hill and told our chief that now, if he would fight, Walpi would give to us that part of mesa toward that end where sun comes up, and also much good land where they could raise some corn.

'But our Tewa chief was very mad. He said those Walpi men told lies. Still, perhaps now they had to fight because, if Utseh killed those Walpi men, then after that they would kill all our Tewa, too. So Tewa men made many arrows. They made some ceremony with Pohaha, who is our god of war. Then they made high bank with dead bodies of some sheep. They hid behind this high place. When those Utseh came, our Tewa shot with many arrows. They fought hard with those Utseh until our sun went down. Then when that darkness gave them rest, those Utseh men were dead. Our Tewa fighters had killed them all, all but two, and to those two our Bear Chief spoke: "You go back home," he said to them, "and tell your Utseh chief that now Tewa Bear, men who can fight, have come to Hopi, and it is they who have killed those Utseh men."

'So those two men, they went back home and told their chief and maybe he was scared, for since that day those Utseh people never have come back to Hopi. Then those Walpi men made line across their rock just east of that town and on one side of line was to be Walpi, on other side new place for Tewa to live. So it was that our Tewa people built their village high on rocky mesa. That village Hopi people always call by their own name of Hano. There we took rock and made our houses, there we made our Katchinas dance. We made some Hopi Katchinas as well, but always we have had our Tewa gods to help bring clouds and rain. To this new place Castile fighters never came at all. Maybe they were scared, maybe it was much too far. Now it has been long time and many seasons have passed since our people came to Hano. Still we speak our Tewa words and make our Tewa ceremony. Still we are mad with Walpi men, but are good friends with people of other Hopi towns.'

When Polakka finished speaking, Sikyanömsi smiled happily and declared: 'It is right. Tewa people are our friends. Some Tewa men come here to live with wives from our Mishongnovi. And one of our men went east to Hano, where now he has Tewa wife.'

While she was speaking, Kwayeshva walked across the room and picked up his drum which the Katchinas had given him many years before. It was not as gaily painted as it had been when Kokle presented it to him, but its booming tone was as rich as ever. Carrying it over to Polakka, who was squatting by the fire, the boy placed the drum before the Tewa man and suggested, 'Maybe now you will sing some Tewa song for us?'

Grunting affirmatively, Polakka took the leather-knobbed stick from the boy, and tapped at the drum to test its tone.

'Nice drum. Who make it?' he inquired.

'The Katchinas give it to 'Yeshva when he was little boy. His father make it and give it to Katchinas.'

Kwayeshva looked up in great surprise. Of course now he was old enough to know these things, but his mind was not yet accustomed to think of the acts of masked divinity in terms of human manipulation. Then, after a few more preliminary drumbeats, the man from Hano sang of the days a hundred and sixty years before when his ancestors had come from the slopes of the Blood-of-Christ Mountains north of the Spanish town of Santa Fe. It was a long song, almost a saga of ancient and warlike days. At its conclusion he handed the drum back to Kwayeshva.

'Maybe you too can sing song?' he suggested.

So the Hopi boy, in a clear, high voice which was just beginning to take on the richer quality of a man's tones, sang a song of the coming of the rain. First he described the land parched by continuous sun heat, then the young green corn plants whose upthrust sheaves were beginning to wither. Then his song became a prayer to the great gods of the four world-quarters. Then his drumbeat quickened as he told of the response of these great chieftains and of how they reached out for the clouds and blew them over to the Hopi fields. Faster and faster Kwayeshva pounded his drum as he sang of the coming of the rain, of the swirling of waters through the dry washes of the desert land, of the pools of water that formed about and slaked the thirst of the withered plants. There was joy in his voice, the joy of a whole people to whom corn is life and for whom drought is a sinister pronouncement of starvation and death.

As he concluded his song, Kwayeshva looked at Butterfly Girl to see if she liked it. Her eyes, positively brilliant with happiness, sent a wave of sudden joy sweeping through the boy's young body. Then Polakka spoke.

'Where did you learn that song?' he demanded. The man from Hano was quite definitely excited. 'That is *fine* song!'

Kwayeshva, confused by the sudden shock of the look he caught in the girl's eyes, hesitated in replying, so his mother spoke up proudly: 'That is 'Yeshva's song. He made that song. He makes many nice songs.'

Polakka was almost incredulous as he looked at the slim young Hopi boy. 'You made that song?' Then, with a broad smile of high approval: 'Some day, 'Yeshva, you will be great singer. Maybe in Anknwa this winter you will come and teach that song to Tewa men. Then you will dance with our Hano people and we shall have fine time.'

The tinkle of bells outside caused 'Nömsi to jump to her feet.

'Katchinas are ready!' she cried excitedly. 'We must go to kiva.'

So hastily throwing their blankets about them they all left the room. Outside, the silver circle of the full moon had turned darkness into near day. The snow had caught the glowing moonlight and reflected it up again so that each house was made luminous, and even the gray forms of the burros who stood about were transformed from fuzzy gray animals into magical creatures painted with quicksilver.

Here and there, near the kivas, groups of costumed men stood huddled together, some of them nearly concealed by shadow, others clearly revealed by the moonlight. One or two men were kneeling, while they adjusted bell straps or other parts of their costume.

Hastily the group from Sikyanömsi's house climbed down the ladder into the first kiva, which stood almost outside the Hopi woman's house. As they entered, a great blast of hot air billowed upward. Within the kiva the men, women, and older children were seated on the raised portion of the kiva floor. They were chatting gaily, their spirits high with anticipation, although it was long after midnight.

As 'Nömsi elbowed her way across the kiva floor, she stopped here and there for a word and a laugh. Frequently men arose and came forward to greet Polakka. Finally they all settled down in a corner. Suddenly the bells tinkled clearly at the kiva entrance. In the center of the kiva, two chiefs had been listening intently for this sound. '*Yungya'ai!*' They shouted their invitation for the gods to enter.

In response, a high, querulous voice was heard from outside the kiva hatchway. It was a thin, reedy, complaining voice. Quietly 'Nömsi whispered to the children that it was the Powamuya grandmother, who is a very fussy and disagreeable person.

For some time the two chiefs and this difficult female shouted to each other. The chiefs wanted the Katchinas to come inside and dance for the people, but for a long time the grandmother was reluctant to bring them in. She said that her men didn't amount to much anyway, that they were always causing her trouble. Occasionally, she would be embarrassingly explicit in revealing intimate details of the marital existence of various members of her family.

All through this dialogue, the audience inside the kiva shrieked with hilarious laughter. There was no hint of pretense in the Katchina grandmother's voice. It was definitely and convincingly that of an aged shrew, with a huge chip on her shoulder, and insistent on proclaiming her wrongs to the world. Not content with informing the chiefs about the life of her sons with their wives, she then proceeded to give utterance to all her suspicions of their extra-marital acts. In fact, as she had said in the beginning, they were all an utterly shiftless lot.

Finally, after much grumbling, she grudgingly consented to enter the kiva, and presently down she came, a thin, weazened creature, and the only one of the Katchina group who wore a mask. This was a highly grotesque affair, a white facial mask ornamented with an amusingly protuberant nose. She wore the conventional costume of a Hopi woman, wrapped buckskin leggings, blue dress, and red-and-white cloak. Following her were a long line of men and boys. Their bodies were bare except for kilts, and to their hair were fastened imitation painted flowers made of corn husks symbolizing squash blossoms, which represent purity — in spite of the grandmother's caustic comments.

The men formed in an arc at the right, the boys at the left facing the audience. The youngsters represented the sisters of the gods, although their appearance was quite obviously masculine. Some of the boys were grinning at their parents seated across the room. They were very young, and for some of them this was their first dance.

The leader of the Powamuya Katchinas stood in the center of the line, his rank indicated by a small crook with a prayer feather attached which he held in his hand. He began the ceremony by telling the chiefs where the Katchinas had come from, and in conclusion he handed one of the village elders a perfect ear of corn. The old man who received this then sprinkled the gods with meal and threw a pinch to the east, where the sun would rise in a few hours.

The old man then stepped back and the Kököinaka, or leader of the gods, signaled with his rattle; the dancers marked the rhythm of their song with four preliminary steps, and then the dance began.

While the people sat radiating pleasure and happiness on the raised floor of the kiva and the chiefs nodded with solemn approval, the semicircle of dancers, keeping time with rattles in their left hands, began to sing. In the center, where the line of men met the line of boys, the two central figures, a Katchina and his sister, joined hands with their palms outward, danced forward and then back, while the rest broke their semicircle to follow them. Three times this was done.

They were dancing with an almost sinuous, gliding motion similar to advancing waves of water thrust forward between two rocks, forward and back until finally it rolls on far enough so that it passes around the two rocks and falls back to where it started. Likewise the dancers, heading the two curved lines of men and boys, for the fourth time gliding forward to the center of the room, relinquished their grip on each other's hand and parted, each returning to the foot of the curved dancing lines of Katchinas and their boy-impersonated sisters.

The next pair did likewise, and so it continued until all the dancers in turn had headed their respective groups. The old grandmother, in spite of her obvious antiquity and acidulous disposition, romped with the line of boys as gaily as any of them.

To Kwayeshva this experience of seeing a night dance

in the kiva was not a new one, for he had witnessed many winter dances; but the sensation of seeing actual Katchinas without masks and obviously impersonated by the men and boys of the village was very strange and a little bit upsetting. During the last few days a most bewildering series of events had taken place — his initiation, all the revelations about the Katchinas, as well as the coming of this girl, in whom he sensed such a definite power to stir up in him strange and altogether disturbing sensations. Then, too, he was tired, utterly worn out by the strain of the ordeal through which he had passed and the lack of sleep for which his young growing body clamored.

The dancers left the kiva and repeated their performance in one of the other ceremonial rooms, their places being taken by an incoming group enlivened by two grandmothers, who scolded not only the men and boys, but each other as well. In each of the five kivas of Mishongnovi the Powamuya Katchinas were dancing, and from one to another of these underground rooms the groups of gods, maidens, and grandmothers went, rotating until each act had been performed twice in each kiva, making ten performances by all of the participating groups.

The thick, hot air, the rhythm of rattles and song and dancing feet, had a definitely hypnotic effect on Kwayeshva and Butterfly Girl, for, after all, they were very young; they were not even quite full grown. From time to time their eyes would slowly close; then a sudden shout or change of rhythm would bring them back to consciousness of the dance and their surroundings. Finally, however, the boy leaned against his mother for a few moments. Then, obeying some sleep-dictated instinct, he turned a little, and stretching first an arm, then a leg, he moved away from his mother until his boyish form became still in the calm of happy sleep.

Sikyanömsi looked at him as he lay with his head just barely touching the shoulder of the slim little Butterfly Girl. Her man-child was striding vigorously now on the path of life, and the steps he was taking were leading him away from her.

XI. ÖSÖ: THE CACTUS THAT KILLS

WHEN they returned to Sikyanömsi's home, the fire on the hearth was extinguished and the room was dark and cold. They were all achingly tired, weary after all the joyous laughter and activity that had drained the strength out of their bodies.

'Yeshva had kindled a fire and his mother had spread sheepskins on the floor for her family and their guests to sleep on, when suddenly an angry, menacing growl was heard from without — a sound that was followed by a blast of cold air that swept into the room as the door was flung open. The dim light of the scarcely ignited fire showed two of the chiefs of the village, and following them the black, hideous form of the flogging god of the Hopi.

Sikyanömsi gasped in sudden dismay. This was no part of the Bean Ceremony — why did they come to her house? Then Letaiyo came in, and his strong face was lined with pain and anxiety. The oldest chief strode across the room until he stood before Kwayeshva, who stared at him, his black eyes that but a moment ago were pinched with sleepiness now wide with uncomprehending panic. The eyes of the chief were narrowed with anger. His voice was harsh and bitter:

'Kwayeshva, Katchinas say you tell small Hopi boy secrets you learn in kiva. When you get whipped, we tell you if you betray secrets of Katchinas that they will come for you and beat you with cactus until you die.'

Poor 'Nömsi gave a sudden stricken cry — her boy, her man-little-one to whom she had twice given birth and whose life was the very essence of her own being — her *tiposi* who had become a man — he *could* not have betrayed his people! Panic in her eyes, she clutched at her oldest daughter for support while the remorseless, biting words of the chief dropped like acid on her heart.

As for 'Yeshva, tired and still a child for all his initiation, his mind, his body had suddenly become as mud. He could not think. He could not act, not even speak while slowly toward him came the flogging god, and into the boy's paralyzed mind there seeped the fact that the Katchina held menacingly in his hand a long spine-covered club of *ösö* — the cactus that kills.

'Kwayeshva' — the chief's voice cut through the fog of the boy's mind — 'you tell Comes-with-Rain that Katchinas don't come from Növatükyaovi. Katchinas know what you do and they say you must be whipped until you are dead.'

Butterfly Girl buried her head in her mother's breast and began to sob. Letaiyo, helpless to aid his son, stood silently watching as the boy still remained mute.

''Yeshva,' he pleaded, 'tell Katchinas what you say to small Hopi boy.'

His father's words brought a partial sense of sanity to the terrified youngster, and slowly the hideous danger in which he stood steadied the boy. Tears spilled out of his eyes and his slim youthfulness was wrenched by sobs as he tore loose from his numbness the words:

'No! No! No! I didn't tell secrets! I *never* said to Comes-with-Rain anything about Katchinas.'

'Kwayeshva' — the grimness of the chief's voice stabbed through the boy's protest — 'Katchinas tell us they heard Hopi boy say to you that Katchinas don't come from Növatükyaovi. How did he know this? How did this boy learn secrets of our people?'

'I didn't tell him,' 'Yeshva pleaded. 'He asked me questions. He asked me what happened when I got whipped. He asked me what I saw in kiva, but I told him he is *kahopi*, he must not ask me those things. I did not *tell* him; he just *asked* me!'

'Hopi boy does not know these things if somebody does not tell him. You are one who told him those secrets of Hopi people, and now Katchina must beat you with *ösö* whip.'

The flogger advanced toward the boy, raising his arm until the needle-covered cactus was poised over Kwayeshva's back.

Desperately Sikyanömsi threw herself between them, trying to take on her own ageing body the punishment that would bring death to her son. Her action roused 'Yeshva as nothing else could have done. Straight as the arrow of his manhood that was thrust into the thatch overhead, he stood before the angry god and the chiefs. Without a quiver or sign of fear he looked straight into the eyes of his accusers.

'You say Katchinas know everything people do! Then Katchinas *know* I do not lie, they *know* boy asked me questions and I told him he is bad and must not talk about these things. You ask Katchinas what I said.

You ask boy what I say. My heart is not ashamed. I did not betray secrets of Hopi people.'

The ring of sincerity in the boy's voice was unmistakable — his face was flushed with confidence as he stood there, his mother clinging to his arm. Butterfly Girl looked up again, hope creeping into her eyes. 'Yeshva's sisters stopped sobbing, and for a moment the room was charged with dramatic silence.

The old chief looked deep and searchingly into the boy's flashing eyes. Slowly the anger died out and respect entered into them.

'I will go get that small Hopi boy,' he said, and walked across the room and out the door.

The seconds stumbled into minutes as time plodded on. There was no sound in the room except the scattered staccato of the cedar fire. Then again the door was flung open and the chief re-entered, dragging after him a screaming child and followed by the small boy's parents. They knew, as Letaiyo had known, the futility of protest against the decision of the priests.

As soon as Comes-with-Rain saw the flogging Katchina, he flung himself into a mad insane paroxysm of shrieking terror, which was only increased by the remorseless voice of the chief asking him the same questions that formerly had been addressed to Kwayeshva. The words of the old man pelted like hail on the boy's fear-sensitized mind.

Finally, instead of the smaller boy, it was Kwayeshva who spoke.

'He can't talk to you,' he said to the chief. 'He is too scared. Maybe you will let me ask him some questions.'

'*Ancha'ai*,' nodded the chief.

So 'Yeshva began:

'Comes-with-Rain, when Katchinas came today with presents, you asked me foolish questions. You asked me about things I saw in kiva and I told you you were *kahopi*, you must not ask those questions. Then you said I think I am big man now because I got whipped by Katchinas and you said I am *quivihoya* because I do not talk to little boys. Do I tell lies, or is that so?'

The steadiness in Kwayeshva's voice had calmed the smaller boy so that he finally managed to utter a husky '*Wi!*' of affirmation.

Then Kwayeshva turned to the chief. 'He is just a small boy who thinks too much,' he informed the old man, speaking from the loftiness of his own greater maturity, for he was a whole half-year older than Comes-with-Rain.

A trace of a twinkle flashed into the old man's eyes, but the whole matter was too serious to be dismissed calmly, even though he was now convinced that Kwayeshva was completely innocent of the charge of betraying the secrets of the masked gods. So he hammered threats at young Comes-with-Rain that if he should ever ask such questions again or talk about these secret things the flogging Katchinas would return, and this time the cactus whip would fall across the boy's life trail and send him to the world of shadows.

Still sobbing, the boy was taken home by his parents; then the flogging god and the chief passed out of the room and into the blackness of the icy night.

It was the man from Tewa who broke the silence following the departure of the chiefs.

"'Yeshva,' he said, putting his hand on the boy's shoulder, 'maybe you are still small Hopi boy, but you speak to chief like one big man.'

Somewhat abashed, Kwayeshva looked about at the others. In the clear light cast by the now blazing fire, he could see tears still shining in the eyes of his mother, his sisters, and — tears even in the eyes of Butterfly Girl. For a moment he was startled. Why should it make him feel that way to see this girl from Tewa cry, when his sisters' tears didn't have that effect on him at all?

For Sikyanömsi the sudden release from the bondage of intense anxiety made her feel that she must do something. She couldn't just curl up and go to sleep, so, covering her emotion by gently scolding her daughters, she made them help her prepare food; and as the first gray shaft of dawn penetrated the black sky of night, the Hopi family and their Tewa friends were finishing the last vestiges of the third serving of the ceremonially grown bean sprouts.

XII. THE PLUMED SERPENT OF THE WATER WORLD

THE next day and for many days Sikyanömsi was acutely conscious of her son's actions. Her dark eyes followed him wherever he went, wistfully, anxiously, and yet with a wealth of such pride that her pulses fairly throbbed with it. That sudden poignant moment when 'Yeshva was about to be lashed with cactus out of her life had blown into flame every glowing ember of her mother love, and now, as he carried cedar logs and threw them down by the hearth, she exulted over his supple, slim strength; and as he laughed and sang his way from dawn to dusk, 'Nömsi, too, sang in her heart her fervent hymn of joy to the gods who had made him strong in his manhood and had been merciful to him when death's shadow lay in opaque blackness over his life's steep trail.

Early one morning, a week after their Tewa guests had returned to Hano, Sikyanömsi, coming out of her door, discovered her son, blanket-wrapped, seated on his horse that snorted twin clouds of frozen vapor into the winter air.

''Yeshva,' she exclaimed, 'where do you go?'

The boy, his brown cheeks flushed with the blood that pounded through his veins, waved toward the west. 'Shongopavi,' he replied. 'Today they have Bean Dance and maybe many Katchinas. I come back tomorrow.'

As he spoke, other riders dashed along the narrow trail, and presently 'Nömsi, totally oblivious to the zero weather, watched them all lope across the snow-whitened sand-dunes until they became black dots drawn westward across the untracked space of desert miles between Mishongnovi and the even more ancient town at the western end of the middle mesa.

At Shongopavi, everywhere there was swift motion, multicolored brilliance, and the same note of joy rippled through the town as had made its sister village triumphant a few days before, because of its successful harvest of beans.

Many Kökelom clacked their way about; presents were handed out to delighted children. Then, toward noon, the gift-giving gods informed the village fathers that, as they had a prodigious amount of work to do, they must leave for their distant home. Still, they announced, they would return again that evening and tell the people all about their adventures during the day. So, after the Shongopavi elders had thanked them for their gifts and after prayer meal had been tossed toward them, the Kökelom departed with impatient gestures and falsetto-voiced argument.

All through the afternoon other gods danced or frolicked, stalked about in majestic dignity, or occasioned hilarious mirth by their absurd antics. As at Mishongnovi, an imitator set fire to his cedar bark head-dress and, crowned with spitting flame, fled from the laughter-echoing plaza.

When darkness followed in the wake of the sun, Kwayeshva and his friends scattered through the village, each one going to the home of some particular friend or relative.

It happened that years ago Sikyanömsi's older brother had married and therefore had gone to the home of his wife, a woman of Shongopavi. As night solidified the darkening shadows, 'Yeshva was seated in the home of his uncle and aunt munching away on the mystically grown bean sprouts. The room was ringing with laughter as the men and women harked back to the most joyous moments of the great day that was drawing to a close. The boy, his face smeared with grease from the food, was grinning from ear to ear with delight over a story his uncle had been telling, when all at once the door banged open and a sudden chill was driven like a wedge into the warmth of the happy, carefree scene.

Others, earlier in the evening, had come and gone, and the opening and closing of the door had let in a little cool air that had immediately been warmed by the blazing heat of the cedar fire; but this time the chill came not so much from the outer air as from the palsied, twisted figure of the weird old man who entered. As the people all looked at him, the smiles on their faces shriveled up and died, while the room in which the high note of laughter had been bounding back and forth became mute with repression. Even the cedar-fed flames seemed to cower on the hearth.

The old man, who was totally blind, stood near the doorway, resenting the joy that was dispelled by his coming, but perceptibly gloating over his power to banish such happiness. His grayish-brown face was covered with wrinkles, like minute canyons, irradiating from his eyes, which were coated with film, like the scum on stagnant pools. His white hair was matted with dirt.

The blanket in which his body was enveloped was encrusted with filth, so that its design could scarcely be seen. One of his battered red moccasins gaped open in front and showed dirty, calloused toes ending in nails that curved downwards like the claws of a bird of prey.

In the hushed silence of the room he stood there, his arms extended and shaking as if they were buffeted by storm. Like a wild beast he sniffed about, sensing the presence of food; then, slowly and stealthily, he groped his way across the floor until his twitching hands found the bowl. Wolflike, he gulped down huge handfuls of stew and beans, while the others sat about tense and motionless, silent. Then, still without a word, he wiped his food-stained hands on the vile blanket, that once had been a thing of beauty, and left the room.

Gradually the hesitant murmur of awe-hushed voices pushed up through the silence. Then, as if to banish the chill and shadow, the man of the house threw a new log on the fire as Kwayeshva, in frightened bewilderment, asked: 'Who is that man? He makes me feel——' The boy hesitated.

His uncle looked about cautiously, but the flame that raced up the huge cedar log gave light that leaped through the shadow. So, in the reassuring brilliance of his warm, fire-lighted home, the Shongopavi man spoke:

'Some men say he is *powaka,* bad man with evil power. He says he is Palalökong, and just as our fathers told us that great Snake God of water world came to live with people long ago in Palatkwapi far south of here, so this old man lives with us now. He makes us think about story, how this Palalökong when he was old got mad at those people in that town because they threw him down in dirty places and laughed at him until he was so mad that he destroyed that whole village with big flood. He makes us remember that in that town nearly every man died because that Palalökong got mad. We know this story is true; that it happened to Patki Clan when they lived in south long before they came to Hopi. We know this old man here is Patki Clan man, and maybe he is right. Maybe he is Palalökong and not just *powaka*, so sometimes we give him food because he makes us scared. We don't want him to be mad and make big flood to kill all our people.'

Just then someone bounded into the room and called excitedly to all those within that it was time to go to the kiva, that soon the Kökelom would return. This sudden interruption cut through the cloud that had hovered over the room, so with almost feverish gaiety the people sprang to their feet, shouted that they were coming, and then hurried through the cold night and down the steep ladder to the heated dimness of the underground ceremonial room.

A very few minutes later the turtle-shell rattles, the high-pitched voices of the gods proclaimed their arrival.

'*Yungya'ai!*' shouted the chiefs. Then the long ladder creaked as the blue-moccasined feet of the two Katchinas came down rung by rung, while the gods carried in their arms great bundles of sweet corn. Placing these on the floor, the two Kökelom climbed the ladder again, and this time reappeared bearing many rolls of red *piki*. A third trip enabled each of them to bring to the assembled people a large watermelon, which, with the other food, was placed by the chiefs in the middle of the floor.

Recently, Kwayeshva had been told that at Mishongnovi, whenever the people celebrate the quadrennial initiation into the Hopi secret societies, the Kökelom always tell a long traditional story to all those whose maturity entitles them to hear it. However, at Shongopavi this intricate and amusing tale is narrated every year by these Katchinas. The majority of the people had heard this story many times, but to Kwayeshva it was excitingly new. So with a thrill of anticipation the boy settled down to listen to the gay, mirth-provoking gods who took the center of the stage and, after the usual preliminary of meal sprinkling and addresses of welcome, began their time-honored speech.

It was obvious that one Kokle was the stronger-minded member of the pair, for he did all the talking, while his brother, at appropriate intervals, chimed in with '*Wi*' or '*Ancha'ai*,' which two words seemed to be the only ones in his working vocabulary.

The talkative god, with highly exaggerated pantomime, said that when they left Shongopavi in the morning they were so afraid they would be late that they ran all the way to Kisiuva, the sacred Shadow Spring to the northeast. However, fast as they had run, they found that they were in for a thorough scolding from their grandmother. These aged women of the Katchina world seem to have a very poor opinion of their children's offspring, for just as the Powamuya grandmother had done at Mishongnovi, the one at Kisiuva left nothing unsaid in caustic disparagement of the Kökelom.

Finally they escaped from her sharp tongue and ran to a distant field, where their grandfather and other relatives were waiting for them. Kwayeshva, his friends, and the people of Shongopavi roared with laughter as one of the Katchinas told how he had tried to help the others take ashes out of the pit in which corn had been roasted, but being unskilled in such a proceeding, he had stirred up the ashes so that he had nearly sneezed himself to death. More fun was occasioned when the god described the feast that followed, and how after eating watermelon some of the girls had pinched the seeds at the silent Kokle, which mark of favoritism had made his brother highly jealous, until, to pacify him, one of the girls pelted him also with seeds, one of which hit him squarely in the eye.

After their dinner was finished, their grandfather insisted on their gathering corn and cooking it in the pit in order that it might be ready to take to the Hopi people that night. When this was done, the old man told the Kökelom to go catch a deer. The dominant member of the pair had been boasting that he was not only a great hunter, but was actually able to tell the exact degree of fatness of a deer by pinching its tail (which absurd statement caused a wave of hilarity to sweep through the kiva). After much hunting, a herd of deer finally was located; so, separating, the two gods stalked them, one advancing from each side of the grove in which the animals were feeding.

Stealthily they crept up on the deer, and the boastful Kokle had just grasped a large buck firmly by the tail when suddenly the animals stampeded, dragging the poor

Katchina through the brush until his hand was finally wrenched loose from the deer's tiny tail; then, while the discomfited god gasped for air, the animals disappeared out of sight.

Completely chagrined, he set out to look for his brother. While he was searching, he discovered to his great delight that a small deer had been run over by the rest, and being stunned, it was easily captured. It was a thin, stunted specimen, scarcely larger than a fawn, but still it was better than nothing, so, swinging it up over his shoulder, the god had just started for Kisiuva when his less assertive brother came up lugging behind him a huge buck which he had killed with his bare hands.

When they reached the Shadow Spring they found that the only Katchina there was their grandfather, who scolded them for being late, and said that it had been planned for them to lead the procession of chief Katchinas to Shongopavi that night; but, as they had evidently been lazy over something, Ahöla and the rest had gone on ahead. So bearing sweet corn for the Hopi, they hurried away. Fourteen stops were made on the road to the Hopi village, at each of which some present was given to the Katchinas by those they encountered to be borne to the kiva-assembled people of Shongopavi.

As they sped through the canyons and over the desert, the sky began to darken and the thunder to crash ominously, while forked lightning jabbed at the earth. Then rain came pelting down until, to the complete dismay of the tardy Katchinas, they came to the banks of an ordinarily dry wash and found there a surging torrent.

Baffled at first, they debated how they should cross.

Finally it was agreed that they would try to jump across the stream, so they made a long running start and dashed toward the broad expanse of water. Just as they reached the bank, the usually silent Kokle made a remark that threw them both so completely out of stride that they stopped short and nearly fell into the foaming stream. Again they tried to leap across the river, and this time the first Kokle hurled himself over the water and just barely landed on the other side. Turning around, he discovered that his brother had lost his nerve and stood hesitant on the farther bank.

So the first one taunted the other until he rushed at the stream, shut his eyes tight, and landed squarely in the middle of the turbulent water. Over and over he turned as the stream bore him rapidly between the tumbling banks of sand. Every time he came to the surface, he signaled his distress by shaking his rattle. The other Kokle, in the meantime, had been racing along the bank, frantically trying to find some place from which he could reach his drowning brother. Finally a protruding sand bar made this possible, so the hapless deity, with his stomach and eyes protruding, was hauled out to safety.

Quickly the more acrobatic Kokle laid his brother face down on the ground and then jumped gaily on his back, which caused the water to spurt out through his mouth until it described a great arc like a rainbow. Slowly the half-dead god regained his strength, and finally they caught up to the chief Katchinas; then acting on the instructions of these mighty gods, they hurried on to Shongopavi to tell the people of all the things that had happened to them, and that in a few minutes the greatest of the Hopi gods would come to the kiva.

As the Kökelom reached this point in their long narrative, Ahöla's strange, eerie cry was heard from without, starting with a deep bass growl and rising in a crescendo to a loud, shrill falsetto. Quickly the two Kökelom gave out the presents that they had brought, and then down the ladder came, first, a Hopi priest, then Aototo, the great white god who is so powerful that in this procession he took precedence over even Ahöla himself. Then came the feathered Sun God, gorgeous and impressive in his superb raiment. After him a Katchina maiden, then the nearly nude, spotted figure of the little Corn God, Kokozhori. Then Aha, the great Soyal Katchina of the Patki Clan, and after him the remaining Katchina maiden.

As Kwayeshva looked at them his thoughts reached back to the storm-ridden day when he had seen these same gods, except for Aototo, come to Mishongnovi, and his uncle Lomavantiwa, as a Katchina maiden, nearly lose his mask through the swirling power of the wind.

First at the Sipapuni, typifying the rectangular place of man's first emergence from the underworld, and later at other important places in the kiva, the Sun God Ahöla bent forward and then back, while his powerful voice roared and then shrilled through the crowded underground room. Finally, bearing the feather-symboled prayers of the people, the gods ascended the ladder and disappeared in the blackness of the night.

Soon after their departure, groups of Powamuya Katchinas entered and danced successively in the different kivas, while their surging, rhythmic movement, joyous and triumphant, swept into the hearts of the people. Finally they all climbed out of the kivas, tired but joyful, and were dispersing to their homes when suddenly they saw the moon shrink back behind a thick, black cloud. Then, tapping its way over the stone and ice, the gnarled figure of Palalökong came toward them out of a wall of shadow until he stood before the whole blanketed crowd.

Behind him a huge pile of twisted cedar logs placed on end against a wall wriggled like gigantic serpents upward into the darkness of the sky.

'You Shongopavi men' — his cracked voice dribbled out of his tight thin lips — 'maybe I say something to you.' He paused and leered about. As he did so a sixteen-year-old boy pranced up before him.

'You old man,' he mimicked in a shrill voice, 'maybe *I* say something to *you*.'

The younger people in the crowd laughed, but the boy's mother darted forward and fearfully pulled her son back into the mass of others.

'*Aie!*' — the old man's anger burst out in strident speech — 'you are just like those people in Palatkwapi. You make mock of old men — then, too, you do bad things with other men's wives.'

'*Aie*, Palalökong,' shouted a young voice from the crowd. 'Maybe you would do those things too if you weren't so old and didn't smell so bad no woman would come near you.'

In helpless fury the madman held his stick up in the night air as if to threaten the speaker, but with yelping laughter a group of boys began bombarding him with hard snow from a drift by the kiva. Finally they were restrained by their uneasy elders — and then they heard the crazed Palalökong, like the snake he called himself, spitting words of venom at them, words of such deadly foreboding that they silenced even the boys and drove the crowd back to their homes. For in the emerging moonlight that made his face shine suddenly as if with power, the man who said he was the Feathered Serpent had flung at the people the prophecy that in four days they were to die.

It was a solemn, thoughtful Kwayeshva who tossed on a sheepskin that night. But finally the vitality of youth won its way through fear, and it was to the consciousness of a day dancing with sunlight that he awoke in the morning.

XIII. RIDING YOUTH SINGS TO THE SUN

March blew in fitful fury across the desert land. The sun gleamed with sudden heat, or grew austerely pale when frozen air from the north battered the gaunt mesas and the clustered houses terraced on their crest. Gods came in endless hundreds, and through their coming turned drab winter nights into color-glowing festivals. Then in April, when the grip of winter had relaxed completely, the Hopi turned from dancing and ritual to hard labor in the fields.

Kwayeshva, riding bareback over the undulating dunes, sang his way eastward. Loping along, his horse's hoofbeats made rhythm for newly created song. The boy's voice rang joyously over the flower-scattered plains. Rabbits darted out from the yellow-blossomed thickness of low-growing shrubs along the trail and then hopped frantically to safety wherever they could find it.

Before him, the eastern mesa, topped by its three towns, cleft the desert like a great stone wedge driven westward through the sand. Past the apex of the great rock his horse loped, and then along a windblown trail under its southern wall. All the time 'Yeshva shouted in song as the release of spring was surging through his veins and finding expression in the joyous tones that could be heard even in grim Walpi, the ancient town that peered over the eastern tip of the mesa's rim.

Below the Tewa village of Hano, the thin trail whipped its way around stupendous boulders broken from the cliff, and then darted upward through a gap toward the eastern edge of the town that the fighting men from far away had built there more than a century ago.

As he slowed down for the last steep incline, 'Yeshva saw two long white objects protruding from a dark cave under a mammoth rock. As he approached, the boy saw that these odd bits of whiteness wriggled about. Then all at once small chunks of clay started popping out from the shadowy interior. By this time the boy had come near enough to see that these cylindrical affairs of white were the buckskin-wrapped legs of a woman.

Amused, the boy stopped his horse to watch, and then, in a few moments, a blue-dressed figure crawled out from under the rock and 'Yeshva discovered that it was Pongkwiyo, Butterfly Girl's mother.

'*Aie*, 'Yeshva. *Öm hakami'i?*' she asked.

'I came from Mishongnovi and looked for small horse,' he replied. 'I found that horse all right, so I left him and came to Hano to see our Tewa friends.'

'*Ancha'ai*,' Pongkwiyo replied with pleasure as she wiped the clay dust off her hands. 'My men, they went to cornfields and Butterfly Girl to Isva for water. Maybe you will ride down to spring and tell her to come home. Then we shall all eat some dinner.'

Pongkwiyo had just started to gather together the hard lumps of clay which she had broken off from the dark recess under the rock, when a shuffling sound caused her to look up. As she did so, she saw the close-set eyes of an angry old man watching her. It was the Bear Chief of Walpi. He looked at the clay, looked at the black hole, and then turned to the woman.

'You got clay from under that rock.' There was an acid note of accusation in his voice.

The Tewa woman looked at him calmly, coldly. '*Wi!* I got clay from under rock!' She looked fearlessly into his small, bitter eyes.

Her self-assurance increased the anger of the old chief. Arrogantly he continued: 'I, Mongwi, told you once to stop. I told you if you get clay from under those rocks they will fall down. Then we shall have no trail.'

The chief's wrath ignited a flame in the woman's eyes.

'Then I tell you, Walpi Mongwi,' she retorted, 'that this is Tewa land. When Mongwi of Tewa village tells me to stop, then I go some other place to find clay, but this place is our land, this belongs to Tewa. Long ago Hopi people made line down middle of mesa and Walpi chief told Tewa chief that all land east of that line is Tewa land.'

The old man stood silent, baffled by the old unanswerable argument. Then, as he turned to go back up the trail, 'Tewa!' he muttered disgustedly. 'Tewa are dogs. Tewa are Walpi slaves.'

'So, you say Tewa are dogs and slaves!' Pongkwiyo's shrill voice followed after him. 'Then I say if Tewa Bear did not come to Hopi long ago, there would be no Walpi today. Walpi fighters would just be scalps for Utseh people to mock at.'

During this tirade, 'Yeshva had been leaning back on his horse surveying the pair. As the chief of Walpi disappeared, the boy turned to his Tewa friend and smiled at her.

'I think maybe people from Hano still are good fighters,' he exclaimed, and then, chuckling, he wheeled his horse about and rode down the narrow trail.

Butterfly Girl and three of her friends came giggling down the steep stone steps carved into the rocky cliffs below her home. She, too, was happy, but instead of song, laughter kept rollicking from her lips. Gone was the shy, silent child who had visited friends at Mishongnovi, for with complete assurance she was poking fun at her friend, Tsapele, whose round, fat form was just barely able to squeeze through a narrow cleft in the rock.

'Maybe some day,' tittered Butterfly Girl, 'you will get bigger and then Tewa people will have to make new trail down to Isva. Or maybe we shall get Owango-zhrozhro to come eat up that big rock so you will get through.'

Tsapele, named for the snow-white sister of a snow-white god, laughed gaily at the thought of this fierce monster devouring rocks for her convenience. The teasing didn't bother her in the least. She was fat and she knew it. Lots of Hopi girls were fat. They married, bore many children, and kept growing fatter until finally they became oversized ghosts in the shadow world.

On down the trail they went, each carrying a heavy water jar, their white cloaks edged with flaming red, their thick, black hair wrapped about corn-husk disks so that it stood out over each side of their heads in the exquisite squash-blossom whorls that have always stood for purity and innocence. When they reached the Isva spring, they saw Kwayeshva waiting there for them. The boy was stretched out on his horse as if it had been a bed, and he grinned broadly at Butterfly Girl, who became suddenly touched with shyness, although she looked up at him with obvious pleasure in her eyes.

'You will get some water for home?' he questioned. It was stating the obvious, but words are so unimportant to youth when smiles can sing their way so much more effectively.

Butterfly Girl nodded; then, following the others, she dipped her narrow-necked water jug into the coolness of the rock-sheltered spring. Before she put the corn-husk stopper in, she held the pot up before Kwayeshva, who took a long, refreshing drink from it. Then, plugging it with the yellowed corn husk, he held the container on the horse's back before him, and with Butterfly Girl trudging along beside him started up the trail, leaving Tsapele and the others giggling with excitement.

The horseback trail is much longer than the steep steps that make a short cut from Hano to the spring, so that as they made their slow way toward the village 'Yeshva had plenty of time to tell his little companion about all the exciting things that had happened to him during the past months; and by the time he drew his horse up in front of Pongkwiyo's house, Butterfly Girl too was chattering away with very little restraint, and telling this boy from Mishongnovi of the hard time she was having learning to make pottery like her mother.

'When I make big pot that is thin all over, I get it made almost to top and then it falls down,' she declared ruefully. 'It is only when I make them thick and ugly that they stand upright.'

'Kwamana, my sister, makes good baskets,' 'Yeshva declared. 'Sometimes almost like ones her mother makes. She is big girl now and this spring she will get married, but she made funny baskets when she was small. They were all loose and had no shape and pieces of *mohu* stuck their ends up and she had hard time to make designs come out right.'

Butterfly Girl giggled. 'That is what happens when I paint bowl. I make cloud designs and eagle's wing and it looks nice when I begin, but when I make it go around that pot to where I start, then I have no room to finish my design, and so I have to end it with only half of that cloud and maybe I have to leave out tip of eagle's wing.'

The slim young girl's shyness had crept away, banished as effectively by 'Yeshva's warm, happy smile as the shadows and cold of winter had been vanquished by the brilliance and glowing air of spring.

When the frost had been lifted out of the ground and the sand and rock heated by the increased power of the sun, the women of the three villages on the eastern mesa had been drawn out of their houses to squat in front of their doorways, there to coil serpentine lengths of wet clay and then to pinch and scrape them into bowls, small pots, and huge water jugs. As Kwayeshva and Polimana strolled up the broad trail, one of the pottery makers, a tight-lipped old woman, out of whom kindness seemed to have been shaken by the constant coughing that wrenched her body, turned to a neighbor.

'*Aie!*' she exclaimed. 'Another Hopi boy that comes after our girls! Why can't they find somebody in their own villages? Our Tewa girls must marry Tewa men. Not those Hopi that call us dogs and slaves.'

'It is Walpi people who are always angry with Tewa and call us bad names,' retorted the other woman. 'This is Mishongnovi boy and those people are our friends.'

'Mishongnovi! Walpi! They are all Hopi, and it was those people who made our Tewa starve when they came from Tsañwadi to fight for these "peaceful people," these Hopitu Shinimu. I say if our girls make husbands of our enemies, we must make big trouble!'

The neighbor looked shrewdly at the thin angular woman, whose bitter eyes were like the sunless depths of a pool that cowered under rocks near-by. In it was water, but instead of the sweet freshness of Isva there was a biting acidity that could drive a thirst-tormented man to utter madness.

'It is right that Tewa boys should find Tewa girls for wives. Maybe, though, you do not just think of that. Maybe you think that because Polimana is daughter of Pongkwiyo, who makes better pottery than you make, maybe you say anything *that* girl does is bad.'

Happily unconscious of this criticism and defense, 'Yeshva and the girl of the Tewa stopped before Pongkwiyo's house. They were radiant with spring, youth, and the increasing awareness of the little ripples of attraction that moved steadily from one to another. For them there was no room in the world for blind old men who were prophets of doom or consumptive women who tried to rid themselves of pain by inflicting it on those whose youth and health made them wing their way joyously along life's trail.

All through the afternoon, Kwayeshva busied himself by chopping wood for his Tewa friends, stopping from time to time to watch the gifted Snow Woman and her eagerly imitative daughter build up the curving sides of delicately modeled bowls. As he swung the precious axe that had been acquired in trade from the white man, 'Yeshva fairly shouted in breathless song. For the power of manhood was sweeping into his being, swelling his slim youth into full-blooded, hard-muscled maturity. Before him lay the desert world, green, for a short season, with the countless millions of tiny plants that had been given brief life by the melted winter snow.

With the twilight came Polakka and his son riding in from the fields. The older man showed his genuine pleasure at seeing Kwayeshva.

'You come to Tewa just at right time,' he exclaimed, grinning broadly. 'Pongkwiyo sometimes has bad pains, so last month in Anknwa I told our men in kiva that when time of peaches comes we will have snow Katchinas dance for us to make Pongkwiyo well. They say *ancha'ai*, so I think maybe you can teach us that song and dance with us when these Katchinas come to Tewa.'

Kwayeshva was thrilled with delight at this invitation. The men of Mishongnovi had always praised his singing and spoken highly of the songs he had composed, but this would be the first time that he had been given the opportunity to create music for the gods to sing. In his mind he could picture them already, those magnificent snow gods with their green-and-white faces, wearing resplendent robes and singing their vocal prayer for the rain; singing the very song that he, Kwayeshva, had made.

Polakka, fully aware of the young boy's feelings, made a further suggestion: 'Maybe tonight I will get those men to come to kiva; then you can sing your song for them.'

All the charm of Kwayeshva's vigorous boyhood flashed into the smile with which he responded to the invitation.

'*Wi*,' he said. 'I shall stay and sing for those men in kiva.'

After Pongkwiyo had taken away the emptied food bowl that had contained their supper, 'Yeshva told the Tewa family about a most exciting event that was about to take place. First he looked around to make absolutely certain that none of the neighboring children were within earshot; then he whispered to Polakka, 'In four days the crow wears green shoes at Mishongnovi and I am going to be Höhmsona because I run faster than other Mishongnovi boys.'

While he continued speaking to Polakka, his next remark was rather shyly addressed to Butterfly Girl, 'Maybe you can come to Mishongnovi and see those Katchinas make races with our people.'

'*Wi*, *ancha'ai*,' declared Polakka. 'We will come. Then maybe you will run after me and cut my hair off.'

'Yeshva laughed. 'Maybe you will run too fast, but maybe I shall try to catch you.'

'Soon we have racing Katchinas here,' the boy Mahle interposed. 'Then we, too, shall tell small children that Angwussi, the crow, will wear green shoes. I do not run fast enough to be Höhmsona, so I cannot cut off anybody's hair, but I am going to be Chil'Katchina, and when I catch some man I shall make him eat some hot chili and then he will be mad.'

Conversation burned like the cedar fire on the hearth, sometimes sparkling into laughter, at other times subsiding to a dull glow. After a long period of silence, a rather worried look clouded Kwayeshva's face.

'You know that man in Shongopavi whose name is Palalökong?' he asked Polakka.

The Tewa man nodded. '*Wi*, I know Palalökong. Maybe he is just bad Hopi man. Maybe——' He paused to make a gesture of uncertainty.

'When Powamuya Katchinas dance at Shongopavi,' Kwayeshva said, 'that old man was very mad. He told those people that in four days they will die. Some people get scared. Some boys just laughed at him. Then when those four days were over, nothing happened, so people just made big laugh, and boys threw stones at Palalökong and made him fall down in dirty places. This Palalökong he got so mad that out of his mouth came something like those *mohu* soapsuds we wash our hair in. Some people got scared and ran away when they saw this old man get so mad. What do you think, Polakka? Is this Shongopavi old man *powaka* or maybe is he that great Katchina, Palalökong, who can make all of us die?'

'I cannot say who he is,' the other man confessed. 'Maybe he is right. Maybe he is real Palalökong. When he says people are bad, he speaks true. Hopi people do many bad things. These Walpi men always make trouble for Tewa and some Tewa men are bad. They do wrong with our girls and sometimes with other men's wives. It is not right that they do these things, and maybe Katchinas will come and make us die as Patki people died at Palatkwapi long ago.'

For many minutes there was the tension of sudden silence in the room, while Polakka with intense seriousness pondered over this disturbing idea.

'I tell you what we do,' at last he told 'Yeshva. 'Maybe it will be like long ago in Palatkwapi. Maybe this Palalökong did not mean those people would die in just four days. Maybe he meant that something bad will happen in four months or perhaps four years. When you go home, you tell Letaiyo that I say we should save food. We should not eat so much. We should put away corn, so that if this Palalökong makes big flood, we can go away to mountains and take food with us so we can eat until he is not angry any more.'

Then he turned to his wife. 'Every day now when you make flour of one corn ear, you take another corn ear and put it in back of room so we shall have food if bad times come.'

'*Ancha'ai.* I do this,' agreed Pongkwiyo. 'Maybe we don't eat so much now, but it is better to be just some little bit hungry than to die when bad times come.'

This being agreed on, Polakka arose and stretched a moment. 'Come, 'Yeshva,' he said as he walked toward the door. 'Now we must go to kiva and you will sing song to Tewa men. Then they will learn to sing when our snow Katchinas come at time of first ripe peaches.'

XIV. WHEN THE CROW WEARS GREEN SHOES

Four times the sun rose and set, and then in Mishongnovi the night air in one of the kivas became almost opaque with the uncontrolled smoke of a cedar fire that mingled with the fumes from the pipes and corn-husk cigarettes of the forty men and boys who were busily working there.

To Kwayeshva, as the night hours pushed their way through time, the scene was as confused in outline as a dream. Songs had been practiced, sixteen different long songs, every word of which must be learned so thoroughly that when the men, masked as gods, sang these prayers to the greater deities of the world-quarters, there would be no uncertainty, no chance for error. Every rhythmic beat of the dance, purposely hesitant or boldly assertive, must pulse with the sureness of each man's heart; every step, every turn, every gesture must be so practiced that it would have as much freedom as if it had been spontaneous action.

Two hours after midnight, the full moon, a silver circle that had found its way to the very zenith, shone down through the kiva hatchway as the men who were to be gods climbed up the long, creaking ladder in a solemn procession. The cool spring air that flowed evenly from the north caught at Kwayeshva's moist body as he climbed with the rest out of the overheated, underground room, but in his excitement he was oblivious to chill. Swiftly the men filed across the plaza to the mesa's edge, where one of the older men held out to the rest an ancient pouch containing sacred corn meal. One after another they all dipped their right hands into the bag, and then scattered to various points along the ledge high above the broad expanse of the moonlit desert.

It was a deeply solemn Kwayeshva who stood there and breathed an earnest prayer into the precious grains, a prayer that he might be worthy to take part in the ancient ceremonies of his people, and a prayer that their songs would be heard by the gods and in consequence the life-giving moisture would be brought by the cloud Katchinas and lowered gently over the Hopi fields. Then the boy cast the minute grains of corn toward the east, toward Kisiuva, the Shadow Spring, where long ago the Katchina and Badger Clans lived, and where in the clear depths of its sacred water the gods of these mighty clans still have their home.

The last to finish his murmured prayer was the Kököinaka, the leader, and as his deeply earnest face glowed in the moonlight with the intense seriousness of religious purpose, the other men stood waiting in respectful silence.

As soon as their leader had turned toward them, the men quickly began to put on anklets of bells and other paraphernalia which had been muffled when they made their silent approach to the eastern ledge. These articles being fastened in place, the Kököinaka signaled, '*Tuma'eh* — let us go,' and took his accustomed place in the middle of a single file. Then, with bells jingling, and the line of men hooting and simulating the cries of birds and animals, the whole procession moved westward toward the plaza.

Just then two old men, the Na'amuh, or 'fathers' of the Katchinas, climbed out of the chief kiva and walked quickly toward the open square, where they met the procession coming from the eastern ledge. For a moment the incoming group of men stood quietly in line the entire length of the plaza until their leader in the center shook his rattle. Then, while rattles and bells marked the rhythm of their song, they danced in the moonlight. Forty men danced as forty gods, while the light on their dark brown bodies revealed each spirited motion.

The night then became vital and charged with life as the dancers pounded with their bare feet on the cool sands. In a steady stream, their song flowed out to the four world-quarters, urging the clouds to loom up over the horizon and give their life-providing moisture to the desert land. As the men sang, the clear night air caught up the deep tones of their song and tossed it back echoing from wall to wall of the dark, silent houses where the people slept.

While the others danced, the fathers walked in a circle about them, tossing small pinches of sacred meal toward each unmasked Katchina. Then, when the ceremony was over, one of the Na'amuh addressed the motionless line that but a moment ago had been charged with the vitality of religious fervor. Addressing them as the deities they represented, he spoke for the people of the village and asked the Katchinas to stay and, when the sun's rays had reached the mesa to the east, to dance again for the people, who on seeing them would be 'full of joy.'

There were two Katchinas who had danced apart from all the rest. These were their uncles, and on this occasion represented Höhua, the cross-legged Katchina, a deification of a crippled but notable ancestor from Mishongnovi. These dancers had been keeping time with the rest in spite of the handicap of being required to dance with their right and left feet in reversed position. When the father had finished his speech of invitation, one of the uncles responded for the Katchinas and agreed to dance in the daytime when the people would be awake.

So, with the fathers leading the way, the entire procession retired to their kiva, and until the first gray light of dawn touched the sky, the night was spent in painting, and sewing masks, and in fastening feathers and other appendages to the proper places.

All through his lifetime that dance stood out vividly in Kwayeshva's memory. It was the most thrilling event that had ever taken place in his young life, for even though he was not masked, yet he had danced as a god and sung his prayer into the moonlight air. In him, boyhood faith in the tribal gods had been a seed that had been given life by the sustaining power of actual experience and which, through all the years that were to come, would continue to grow steadily, being rooted firmly in unswerving faith.

In the semidarkness preceding dawn, the men who had danced in the night quietly slipped out of the kiva, and, carrying their masks and other paraphernalia concealed in bundles under their arms, they proceeded to the eastern ledge. At this Katchina house the masks were carefully placed in a line, and the men waited for the dawn to bring light so that they could attend to the final acts of putting on green spruce collars and tying on, or arranging, any feathers that were loose.

Finally, just as the sun rose, the time came for Kwa-yeshva for the first time to wear a Katchina mask. The mask of Höhmsona had been made for him by his god-father, who stood on the ledge by the boy. Acting on in-structions from his godfather, 'Yeshva spat into the mask as an act of purification. Then quickly he put it over his head and took his place with the rest.

For a moment the boy's thrilled sensation over being an actual god was replaced by his uncomfortable awareness of the stuffiness of the mask and the fact that it was pressing his nose flat against his face. He knew that the masks of the racing Katchinas were made with eyes larger than the tiny slits cut in the helmets of the other deities, but even so, Kwayeshva found that it was exceedingly difficult to see clearly. Still, under no circumstances must he stumble, for to an unusual degree his honor was at stake. He had been allowed to participate as the hair-cutting god Höhmsona in spite of the objections raised by several of the old men, who had claimed that the boy was too young and inexperienced to take this important part in the annual ceremony of the racing gods.

Still, the fact remained that he could outrun any of the other boys in the village. His godfather, who had urged the others to allow 'Yeshva to take part as Höhm-sona, was particularly anxious for the boy to impersonate an important Katchina because it is well known that the first mask worn by a Hopi boy indicates definitely the god that he will become when he passes to the spirit world.

In the village many of the mothers, as well as the

few fathers who remained in evidence, were telling their mystified children that 'today the crow wears green shoes.' This was very exciting, and a bit bewildering, especially to the tiny youngsters who scanned the heavens eagerly in the hope of seeing this peculiar phenomenon. Some of the older children had become aware of the fact that as Angwussi, the crow, used to be a racing god, and as the majority of all masked deities wear at times moccasins covered with soft turquoise paint, this cryptic expression heralds the arrival of the Wawas, or racing Katchinas.

As the gods were seen approaching the village from their eastern ledge, the whole town grew tense with excited anticipation, for one of the most vivid, spectacular ceremonies of the Hopi was about to begin. There were more than twenty different kinds of Katchina in the swarming, darting, circling, prancing mass that swept into the plaza. Each one postured, or acted in the manner traditional to the being he represented. Totcha, the humming-bird, circled about with graceful swooping motions, while his arms were extended like wings. The other bird Katchinas, Keesa, the chicken-hawk, and Palakwaiyo, the red-tailed hawk, ran about with the swift approach with which these birds usually pounce upon their victims. Kona, the chipmunk, and Manangaya, the green lizard, darted up on kivas or rock piles with light-footed ease, while the two uncles, Höhua, their legs completely crossed, waddled awkwardly about. They were absurdly overdressed, and wore masks topped with sheepskin wigs which were adorned with imitation flowers. The Tchökapölöluh, or mud-throwers, represented by young boys, lagged a bit behind the rest.

Kwayeshva and another Höhmsona pranced about brandishing sharp-edged knives, and all the time the village echoed with shrill calls and hoots that were muffled by the tight-fitting masks. Then suddenly the Katchinas stopped prancing about, and as they had done during the night, stood in a silent row while the father of the Katchinas spoke to the people and told about his presumably accidental meeting with these gods in the middle of the night, and that he had persuaded them to stay and dance for the people during the daytime.

The Kököinaka, who represented a green-rattle Katchina, or Aya, wore a mask that was made in exact imitation of the design of the lurid, colored toy with which Kwayeshva had played when he was a year-old child strapped to his cradle-board. At the conclusion of the old man's speech this leader of the gods shook his rattle; then the long line of thirty-eight gods, with the two uncles toddling about beside them, began their dance.

Facing the north, they sang to the yellow clouds in that direction to come, and, 'piled on top of each other, to rain down,' and while they danced they sang, their strangely vibrant tones rendered eerie by the masks, lifting their feet so high and touching the ground so lightly that they seemed to be buoyant creatures floating in the air. Their arms were extended horizontally with the ground, and their actions dramatically symbolized the oncoming clouds that were being summoned from the four quarters of the earth.

The two Höhuam tried valiantly to keep pace with the rest, but the strained position of their crossed legs made their motions heavy and awkward. Still, as the dance progressed, their feet became straighter and their movements lighter as the emotional appeal of the dance caused them partly to forget their rôle.

The sun pushed its rays up over the eastern housetops, bisecting the plaza into two long rectangles of shadow and light, bordered with the red-and-white costumes of the women and the blue shirts of the older men, who sat in front of the houses. The roofs were a gallery for the younger men, whose legs dangled over the edge, making a grotesque fringe that hung over the heads of those below.

Everywhere there was the peace of sheer joy and content as the long line of Katchinas danced on in rhythmic personification of faith in the favorable answer to prayer; of confident expectation of rain that would come and bring strength and growth to the young green corn plants that struggled toward maturity in the sandy fields.

As the dancers maintained their vigorous abandon, without a trace of break in their perfect rhythm, the fathers walked about them tossing pinches of sacred meal toward the Katchinas as they had done during the night. Three times the Katchinas danced on the eastern, southern, and western sides of the plaza; then the fathers laid down a single line of meal extending from the village square to the eastern ledge, and the dancers followed it to the place of retirement.

It was a flushed, excited Kwayeshva who took off his mask at the Katchina house and looked out across the sand-dunes to the east. Just as he had hoped, in the distance he saw four horses loping along, and even though they were still so far away, he could distinguish a flash of red in the costume of two of the riders. He smiled happily, quite certain that these four visitors were his Tewa friends coming to see him dance.

Once more the masked gods dashed across the sand and rock from the concealed ledge and danced as before. They were just finishing their rhythmically expressed prayer on the western side of the plaza when the vigorously leaping god, Höhmsona, who before masking had been the Hopi boy, Kwayeshva, saw Polakka and his family walk into the plaza from its southern entrance and cross over to where Sikyanömsi and her three daughters were sitting. While his lips repeated the words of his prayer to the blue clouds of the west, Kwayeshva kept wondering if Butterfly Girl would be able to tell which Höhmsona he was. As he considered the matter, he saw the young Tewa girl looking directly at him, and the sudden happiness he felt over her recognition of him welled into his vibrant song for the rain.

In the corner of the plaza, little Butterfly Girl leaned over and whispered into 'Nömsi's ear:

'I know which Katchina is 'Yeshva. Other Höhmsona has legs that are too fat.'

Sikyanömsi nodded. She had spotted her son the minute he came into the plaza, and was quite as thrilled as he over the momentous event. What an important step this was on his trail of life! From now on it would be marched hand in hand with the gods.

An hour or so later, when the Katchinas had completed their dance for the third time, Pongkwiyo, speaking softly, told 'Nömsi that she had brought something from Tewa that was to be given to 'Yeshva. So toward the conclusion of the fourth dance, the two women walked over to the house at the head of the sandy trail, and presently 'Nömsi staggered across the plaza carrying a huge bundle of food wrapped in cotton cloth. From all parts of the village other women likewise came and made their way to the Katchina ledge, where bundle after bundle was given to their men, who, as gods, so earnestly had been looking after the welfare of the tribe.

As in the early morning, the masks were carefully placed in a row on ground that had been carefully swept. After the food had been presented, the women sprinkled meal on the line of masks and returned to the village. 'Nömsi as she passed had smiled happily at her son, and 'Yeshva in supreme content had grinned back at her. When the women had departed, one of the older men then took the choicest morsels of food from each bundle and placed them at a near-by shrine as a food offering to the Katchinas they represented, in order that just as Kwa-yeshva's unborn spirit had done, the gods might inhale the soul of the food. Early in the preceding evening, the masks had likewise been fed by having a small bit of honey placed inside each helmet near its mouth.

From the ledge where the men, hungry from the violent exercise of their dance, ate heartily of the food brought by the women to the houses where guests were assembled, all through the village there was happy feasting. At Sikyanömsi's house, the chattering voices of the people flashed sound that was translated from dancing sunlight. 'Nömsi had worked for days, cooking every sort of food of which the Hopi knows in anticipation of the great event. For hour after hour she had rubbed her batter-moistened hand over the smoking *piki* rock and peeled off layers of parchment, not only the usual blue kind, but red and white layers as well. Then she had baked mush in a deep pit after carefully chewing some of the ingredients in order that her saliva might make it ferment properly. This *someviki* she wrapped up carefully in little corn-husk bundles.

When afternoon came, the town teemed with excitement, for every man in the village knew that he would be required to race with the gods and demonstrate, if he could, his physical fitness by outrunning them. He knew perfectly well that, if he failed to do so and was caught, he would be punished in one of a variety of ways, depending on the characteristic method invariably employed by each victorious Katchina.

The two Höhuam, obviously impressed by their importance as masters of ceremony, spread blankets out on the ground, and on these were laid parcels of food brought from the Katchina ledge. Then, while the women tittered and chattered in pleased excitement, the first man was selected from the crowd by one of the cross-legged Katchinas, who made most caustic, disparaging comments about the man who had been chosen.

'Look at him,' he jeered in a high falsetto voice. 'He is too fat. Probably he is lazy and eats too much.'

The man, who did have a decided paunch, grinned good-humoredly, and the women, particularly his relatives, shrieked with glee as one of them called out to Höhua: 'Yes, it is so! We have to work hard to get food for him.'

As this bantering dialogue continued, one of the rattle Katchinas stepped up and stood beside the man at the southern end of the plaza. For a moment they eyed each other appraisingly, while the Höhua counted slowly, '*Sökya — löyi — paiyo — nalöyi* ——' Then suddenly at the word 'four' the man, with surprising speed considering his size, ran, while the Katchina, who brandished a formidable yucca whip, followed in swift pursuit.

At the north end of the plaza, with arms outstretched, were two most erotic masked females: the Kokopöl Mamant. Straight toward one of these the runner darted, but just as she was about to seize him he sidestepped, and at that moment the other maiden caught him by the arm, and, being a powerful creature, pulled him down on the ground. The women — related to the victim on his paternal side — elbowed their way out of the crowd and ran to his rescue, while the rattle Katchina, seeing his opponent caught, trotted back to the north end of the plaza.

'You leave our man alone,' one of the women shouted to the victorious Kokopöl Mana. 'You are no good. You can't cook — and you ought to stay home and work instead of chasing after our men.'

The husky pursuer had the man flat on his back by this time, and the rescuing women then proceeded to haul off the apparently oversexed female, who thereupon abandoned her intentions and withdrew from the contest, while the man brushed himself off and laughingly accompanied his relatives to the sidelines.

The second racer was more successful, for competing with Kona, the chipmunk, one of the fastest of the masked racers, he eluded his pursuer the full length of the plaza and also dodged successfully the Kokopöl Mamant as they attempted to waylay him.

A third man, however, being chased by the Chil'-Katchina, was caught halfway down the course and suffered the penalty of defeat by having his mouth crammed full of red-hot chili. Sputtering and gasping, the unfortunate victim made for his house, while other men took his place and raced with the masked gods.

Late in the afternoon, Kwayeshva made his way over to where Polakka was sitting and handed the man a *wiki*, connected rolls of red *piki* tied together with corn husks. Smiling broadly, the man from Tewa accepted the present and the implied invitation to race. Butterfly Girl and her brother Mahle jumped to their feet with excitement, and Sikyanömsi climbed up on a cedar log so she wouldn't miss seeing the exciting event that was to take place. Then, while the cross-legged uncle counted slowly and deliberately, the slim young god, who, having raced several times, by now had become accustomed to his limited vision and to the tight confinement of the mask, eyed his stalwart opponent expectantly. Butterfly Girl was watching him, his mother was almost falling off the log in her excitement, so he *must* win. Polakka dashed through the plaza at the conclusion of the word 'four,' and twisted his body skillfully out of the clutching grasp of the amorous females, but after him, as straight and as swift as an arrow's flight, darted the tall, slim Höhmsona.

Just as they were reaching the farthest limit of the open square, 'Yeshva reached out, caught the flowing black hair of the Tewa man, and with a swift motion of his knife cut a lock from his friend's hair and held it up triumphantly, while Polakka, looking just as much pleased as if he had won the race himself, turned and walked back to his family.

For hours the racing continued; Letotovi, the jet-black racer, smeared sticky, black corn smut over those he caught. Növanchichiklauca, a bi-colored deity, tore his opponent's shirt, while little Tchökapölöluh, being a very small boy, never could catch anyone, and in consequence threw mud at them instead.

All through this joyous ceremony, the venomous old man Palalökong, who had forced one of the men to bring him from Shongopavi, had hobbled about the edge of the crowd. Since his prophecy had been unfulfilled, he had been increasingly jeered at by the younger men until his actions became so uncontrolled that at times he lost his senses completely and at other moments flung a wide variety of curses and prophecies about, to which few people paid the slightest attention.

It was just at the close of the day, after a final dance by the Katchinas, that Palalökong got a chance to be heard. Fumbling his way, he climbed to the top of a kiva roof. Then, snarling, he spat a new prophecy at the people:

'You think — because Katchinas dance — maybe you will get rain.' His film-covered, disease-encrusted eyes twitched with the emotion that drove powerfully through the weakness of his ancient body. 'You think — maybe corn will grow.'

The tremors that shook his body increased as with thick, almost indistinguishable words he slobbered at the men before him: 'I say — *no*, I — Palalökong. I say — no rain will come; I say — all corn will die.' The shaking spread to his whole twisted body, and spume oozed out of his lips. 'I say — all Hopi — will — die!' His words screeched into high-pitched hysteria.

For a moment he tottered above them, and to the people he seemed evil incarnate. Then all at once he pitched forward and fell from the kiva roof in a crumpled, twitching heap before the people, who drew back in very real fear and left him in the shadow-deepening dusk.

Polakka had been one of those who stood near-by. The Tewa man was silent and thoughtful as he walked through the passageway to Sikyanömsi's house, where presently they were joined by a radiant Kwayeshva, brimming over with happiness that swept through his body, as song earlier had leaped from his mask-covered lips.

XV. THE HIGH PLACE OF THE GODS IS BARREN

Four days passed, four days of crystal-sparkling sunshine, for from dawn to dusk the sun's rays shone directly on the earth. They were not impeded by even the tiniest cloud.

Vainly the Hopi looked toward Növatükyaovi, but the western home of the gods seemed to have been abandoned by the cloud Katchinas. Not even the faintest swirl of mist touched its upcurved, shimmering slopes.

Then, when the sacred mountains flamed from the descent of the sun behind them, the men who had taken part in the dance met at the home of their leader. It seemed obvious that some one of them was at fault, so the Kököinaka probed and questioned to see if any man had nullified the power of the ceremony by eating food containing salt at any time during the four days preceding the dance. Or it was quite possible that one of them had slept with his wife during that period. However, if that were the case, the man kept it a dark secret, hidden in the privacy of his own thoughts. Finally the leader turned toward Kwayeshva, who was squatting on the floor with the rest.

'Maybe it is you,' he suggested. 'When you went to Hano, maybe those Tewa gave you food with salt?'

'*Wi*, I ate food there with salt,' the boy answered, 'but that was five days before dance.'

The older man accepted the boy's statement unquestioningly; then for a time there was silence. The Kököinaka looked long and searchingly at each of the men, one after another, who filled the small room of his home. The eyes of all seemed to tell the truth. Then, too, it was incomprehensible that any Hopi man, knowing the imperative need for rain, would cause it to be withheld by violating the sacred rules of the tribe.

'Some man *must* have done wrong, or rain would have come,' the leader insisted. Then, as a sudden thought struck him, 'Unless ——'

A middle-aged man seated by the hearth gave expression to the thought that was creeping into the leader's mind: 'Unless,' he said, 'it was that Palalökong, of Shongopavi, who said he would make water stay away.'

'*Ai!*' interrupted another angrily. 'That man is not Palalökong! You are foolish to think like that!'

'Maybe so,' retorted the leader, 'but if that man is not Palalökong, then why does rain not come to Hopi when we dance?'

A few miles away in Shongopavi, the same thought was agitating the minds of the people. While they had no personal responsibility in the racing Katchina ceremony that recently had been held, still the failure of the rain to come was a matter that concerned every one of them. The change in the attitude of the people toward the madman who believed himself to be a reincarnation of the Feathered Serpent, god of the water world, became more and more marked. As the women began to seek him out with offerings of food, the old man, gloating over the fulfillment of his last prophecy, sneered at them, even though he devoured the mutton and corn they brought to him.

'You people think you can make mock of Palalökong.' There was a wild note of laughter in his voice. 'I told those Mishongnovi men that — their Katchinas will not bring rain if I tell it to stay away.' Once again his shrill, eerie laugh sent chills like icicles shooting through those who heard him.

Some days after that, the crow wore green shoes at Shongopavi, and although the gods danced and raced, and although prayer sticks and sprinkled meal were given to the Katchinas, still the sun moved serenely through an unspotted field of blue, and more and more meetings were held, while the cackling blind man clawed at the people with his scorn, and mercilessly compelled them to give him everything he wanted.

The men of Walpi, Hano, and the intermediate village Sitchumovi danced as gods, while far to the west the men of Oraibi put on their ancient masks and pounded the earth in rhythm for the rain, which did not come.

The gaiety and fun that usually bound through a town when two lives are merged were stilled to sober ritual when a man of the Bear clan of Shongopavi came in May to mate with 'Nömsi's daughter Kwamana.

It was a severe blow to the mother that lack of water for plastering made it impossible to build an added room for her first married child. So when her new son-in-law, in reversal of tradition, took Kwamana across the dunes to his mother's larger home in Shongopavi, 'Nömsi felt that more than the intervening miles had come between her and her daughter. She sensed that the broken custom was a black shadow falling between two closely knit lives.

All through the spring Letaiyo and his son had worked frantically in the cornfields in order that the still-green plants might be given every opportunity to survive to maturity. The winter snow had soaked deep down into the desert earth, so that the searching roots of the corn were still able to find traces of moisture, although the sun beat down with increasing heat day after day. Isva, Toriva, and the other springs still held some of their cooling waters, but every drop was precious, and none of it could possibly be used to aid the plants.

One day late in June Polakka and his son Mahle rode over to Sikyanömsi's summer home, the little shack near the cornfields. And as they sat in the thatched-roof shelter in front of the one-room house, they debated what should be done.

'I think maybe those corn plants in my field will be all right,' Polakka declared. 'They are small and now they begin to get yellow, but still they will grow little ears before they die.'

Letaiyo looked around sadly. 'My peaches are no good,' he said. 'They dried up and fell off our trees. Those beans will not grow. Just maybe some small corn. Still, we have done as you said we should do. We don't eat much. We save our corn. I have killed all our sheep before they died from hunger. Their meat we have dried, and we shall eat that if bad times come. Tomorrow 'Yeshva and other Mishongnovi boys have rabbit hunt, and next week we have our Katchin' Nimana. Then our gods go home to Növatükyaovi. I think Katchinas when they dance want to bring rain to Hopi people; but maybe they are scared of Palalökong because he is Katchina of all that water world.'

'Nömsi brought food and set it before them, but it was a meager fare: a stewed prairie dog and a little corn. She was thinner already, for she allowed herself just enough food to give her strength to continue working in the house and occasionally weaving plaques.

The next day Kwayeshva and some fifty other boys and younger men painted their faces a dull red, and in the early light of morning they rode down the trail to the sun-baked desert below. Some of them loped through the sage and rabbit bush and went to the west; others to the east and south until a gigantic circle had been formed. Then, gripping their curved rabbit sticks, this huge ring of shouting youths rode toward each other in a rapidly diminishing circle. Enormous jack rabbits leaped in fright from the security of little bushes; small cottontails hopped in bewilderment with the rest, not knowing where they were going, but obeying a blind impulse to flee from the pounding horse hoofs that drove them forward.

Closer and closer the ring of men was drawn until all at once it narrowed down to a small circle in which there was a heap of squirming, writhing gray fur, jumbled together in a panic-stricken mass. Swift, skillfully directed motion of sharp-edged rabbit sticks ended their short lives, and then a troop of triumphant boys and men, singing exultantly, rode in the center of an advancing cloud of dust across the rolling sand-dunes and up the steep trail to Mishongnovi.

Sikyanömsi was delighted when her son contributed three long-legged victims of his skill. All food was welcome these days, and then, too, the fur could be cut into long strips and woven through a coarse cotton mesh into blankets that would keep them warm when the winter winds swept relentlessly from the north.

Toward the end of July, the men of Mishongnovi, and later those in the other villages, celebrated the farewell ritual of the gods. The first fruits of the harvest, which are always presented at this time, were stunted ears of corn and but little else. As in the Powamuya, presents were given to the children, and all through the intense heat of a sun-flooded midsummer day the Hemis Katchinas tapped the ground solemnly to the rhythm of the corn-grinding maidens who knelt before them. The Spotted Little Ones, a pair of minute, black deities dotted with color, made lateral motions with their hands in order to summon the rain clouds that so long had stayed away. Then the slim little Katchinas motioned downward with their fingers to symbolize the falling raindrops that were so desperately needed all through that plant-withered, sun-tortured land. The next morning the snow-white god, Aototo, mightiest of Katchinas, conducted a long and carefully planned ritual at the entrance to the chief kiva before he led his fellow deities on their trail to the western mountain. Still, even then, the mesa-edged horizon showed no traces of cloud; still, a flaming sun made waves of intense heat shimmer as they rose from the scorching sands.

The men who make the Wuwuchim Kiva their club-house were the ones who had been in charge of the farewell ritual that year, and it was a discouraged group that gathered there at night four days after the gods had departed. Vainly they hunted for a reason to account for the utter failure of their ceremony. The personal conduct of each member seemed to have been beyond reproach. The songs, the dance steps had all been practiced with unusual thoroughness, and nothing had occurred in the ceremony itself that could in any way mar its efficacy; and yet there had been no rain.

From Oraibi to Hano thought grew to conviction that the blind man, Palalökong, unquestionably was responsible for the drought, and week after week the old man's power grew. Everything possible was done to propitiate his wrath. His every need was anticipated. While others denied themselves, Palalökong ate voraciously until overindulgence made him ill. Then, in a terrific frenzy, he accused the people of Shongopavi of trying to poison him, and snarlingly refused the herbs with which they tried to make him well.

In the Tewa village, the usually joyous, carefree people had become watchful, grim-faced men and women, constantly on the alert to avoid anything that would anger the gods, and seeking desperately for some effective way to summon the rain clouds. The men working in the fields deliberately had walked barefoot over the hot sands that almost seared their feet in the hope that this would make the clouds take pity on them and send cooling rains that would bathe, not only their blistered feet, but the desert land as well. Dance after dance had been held, and on the departing Katchinas smoke had been blown in order that when these dancing deities reached their distant home the greater gods might smell the fumes of the cloud-like smoke and unleash their moisture-bearing messengers, and send them to pour their substance upon the dying corn.

In Polakka's kiva the men were practicing the songs and steps of the Snow-Katchina Dance, and 'Yeshva, bursting with pride, was an important member of the group. Every night until the black hours before dawn, the ceremony was rehearsed; and as the Mishongnovi boy heard the song of his own creation booming forth from the lips of thirty men, he experienced a thrill of ecstasy at hearing his work become vitalized by the combined strength and fervor of the men; then, as the time of the ceremony approached, his faith steadily increased until he became certain that this song of his would bring the rain.

Pongkwiyo, her sisters, and their daughters were busily engaged day after day in preparing food for the Tewa snow gods. This was no time for hoarding, and even though they deprived themselves to the point of aching hunger, still the gods must have an abundance of food, or they would become angered and refuse to send the rain to the people who had danced for it in prayer.

Then, early one morning, over the rocky brow of the eastern ledge, the tips of pairs of eagle tail feathers, then the green-and-white masks of the Pong Katchinas were seen. Sikyanömsi, Letaiyo, and their daughters had all come to Tewa the day before, and as the rising sun shone on the colored magnificence of the incoming gods, the mother's heart was beating so rapidly with excitement over the prospect of hearing her son's song that the fact that this was to be a dance for rain became for a moment a matter of secondary importance. Then, as the snow gods who had come two hundred years ago with the Tewa warriors from the mountains beyond the great river in the east began their dance, 'Nömsi let her thought flow skyward as 'Yeshva's song came to her ears; it was no longer the song of a young boy who sought to entertain guests from a distant town, for into it had gone the pent-up hope and urgent need of thirty men who were singing with full realization that their very lives were at stake. Hunger and inevitable fear had entered every home, and now, if their faith was great enough, the wave of sounds that rolled across the desert might reach to the height of the mountain peaks where the great gods lived, then take form as rain-charged clouds and sweep across the desert plains and back to the town, where Tewa men and a Hopi boy danced in the hot, dry village square.

Still all through the morning there was no response from Növatükyaovi. Then in the afternoon for a short time the people forgot their anxiety and need as the Koyala, the black-and-white-striped fun-makers, came chattering and gesticulating into the plaza. Their painted faces, surmounted by corn-husk horns, were made grotesque by white rings drawn around their eyes and mouths. Over the housetops they scampered and dashed, frolicking and teasing each other as well as the amused spectators. Finally, two of them came in dressed as a burro, the combined legs of the two impersonators serving as the four legs of the animal. With whoops of glee, the Koyala lassoed the absurd burro and harnessed it so that they were enabled to ride triumphantly into the village square.

When these fun-makers left, the laughter that had given sudden relief to the tension of the people subsided into silence as they looked up into a clear blue sky in which there was no trace of cloud. Four times in all did the Katchinas dance; then, just as the fathers of these gods began to address them with a speech of grateful appreciation, one of the Tewa men came running into the plaza and shouted excitedly to the rest that coming from Növatükyaovi was a small cloud, tinged with gray.

Scrambling over each other in their excitement, the people rushed to the housetops; and as the Katchinas stood in a solemn line and received the sprinkled meal and prayer sticks of the men and women, two aged priests stood on the kiva roof and blew great clouds of smoke toward the western sky.

With maddening deliberation, the cloud crept slowly through the sun-filled space from the west. Then, at last, the people, many of them shrieking their excited joy, saw a wall of straight lines extend from the cloud to the earth, and they knew that at last the rain was walking over their desolate fields. As it reached the Tewa village, there was a frantic rush for pots and bowls in order that every possible drop of the precious moisture might be caught.

Kwayeshva, marching toward the ledge with the other Katchinas, had felt the drops of rain fall on his painted body, and into his tired brain there bounded the thought that even if only a few drops came, still the gods were sending it as a sign of their recognition and acceptance of his song.

For some minutes the rain came pelting down, and

then the cloud passed on to the east until there was only the blue sky and steam ascending from the hot rocks that for a moment had been sprinkled by the rain.

Vainly the people looked toward the west in the hope that this cloud was a forerunner to announce the arrival of others; but the Snow-High-Place of the Gods, no longer white, no longer snowclad, reared its rocky crest into a clear-toned crimson-and-yellow sky in which there was not a wisp of cloud to sustain the hope of the people.

XVI. THE POUNDED PRAYER OF THE ANCIENT SNAKES

When August came, renewed confidence swept through Hopi like a cooling breeze; for the time was at hand when the ancient rain-producing ceremony of the Snake people was to be held in some of the villages. In the remaining towns the men of the Flute Society prepared to dramatize their arrival centuries ago when, according to legend, they had won admission to the Hopi villages by their miraculous ability to produce rain and to make corn grow in a single day.

The sun shot down in a life-withering blast as Letaiyo and the other painted priests of the Snake Society searched for their clan brethren who lurked in the rocks and sands of the heat-drenched plains. For many months they had watched carefully for every sign that would enable them to find the habitations of the rattlesnakes. In one hand Letaiyo carried a small wooden hoe and in the other a pair of wing feathers from a buzzard, while over his back he had slung an empty sack.

Swiftly he walked through the sage and greasewood until he could see if the rattler that lived there were coiled under a bush — although the heat of the sun made this improbable. Then, as he saw no sign of the snake, he dug vigorously into the ground with his hoe.

Before him a small mound of earth grew steadily, until

all at once a streak of yellowish-brown flashed before him; and then Letaiyo looked into the glinting eyes of a coiled rattler, whose fangs darted toward him with the swiftness of forked lightning. Warily and with slow deliberation the Snake priest crept toward his hissing brother of the lower world, while he held in one hand the pair of feathers.

All at once the reptile struck and the Hopi man threw himself backward as the serpent whizzed toward him. Again it coiled, and once more the priest of the Snake Society crept toward it while he motioned with his buzzard feathers. This time he was able to approach near enough so that the soft tips of the plumes gently stroked the rattlesnake's back. Slowly, with seeming reluctance, the rattler began to straighten out. Then, as soon as the last coil had unwound, Letaiyo, steadily stroking his clan brother from the world under the earth, pounced on the snake with his free hand and gripped it firmly just below its venom-filled head.

Then, with complete unconcern, he popped the twisting rattlesnake into the empty sack, picked up his hoe, which he had laid at one side while he stalked his victim, and strode through the desert brush to look for another snake.

Every day for four days the men of the Snake Society hunted thus over the hills and plains, and on their return brought the captured reptiles to the kiva of their ceremonial order. The rattlers, bullsnakes, and other serpents were put in narrow-mouthed jars almost identical with the water jugs that were borne by the women up and down the steep trail to Toriva. These pots were then placed in a cave sacred to the powerful beings of the snake world.

When the ninth day of preparation dawned, Sikyanömsi stood in front of her house while 'Yeshva sprawled at her feet in the dusty doorway. A red-hot sun was lifting itself out of a crimson dawn, and already its heat came from the east, pouring across the helpless desert that had been seared with such a succession of flame-shot days. Two tiny wisps of cloud like loosely pulled cotton down stretched lazily along the sun's path. Then, as the fiery circle mounted toward them, the little tufts of sky-held moisture grew tinier until, all at once, there was nothing there but blue space tinged with yellow and an ascending furnace that shot forth air like rivers of molten flame upon the earth, on which no vestige of green could be seen except the dauntless cactus that daily grew more and more wrinkled as it resisted the drought.

'Nömsi had watched the little clouds until the moment of their dissolution; then, as she stared for a moment into the unspotted arc of the sky, her ageing face seemed to contract with pain, the mental pain of despair. For months now she had eaten barely enough food to sustain life. The shriveled ears that were their entire harvest must either be saved or be given to the children and the men. The brown face, across which smiles and laughter had played so continuously, had become a parchment mask through which her high cheekbones protruded with increasing visibility.

From the sky the woman's gaze descended to the roof of the kiva of the Snake people, almost in front of her house. A bow from which red horsehair hung was fastened across the projecting ladder poles that stretched skyward through the roof. Near-by, scattered about, were a number of the wooden hoes that recently had been put to effective use in routing the snakes from their underground homes.

'Those Snake people *must* bring us rain,' she said to her son, 'or else — maybe we all shall die.' There was no trace of hysteria in her voice, no theatricalism, but just a plain recognition of fact.

As she finished speaking, Letaiyo and a number of other men walked across the small open space and descended into the kiva.

'They are going to wash those snakes,' Sikyanömsi whispered to her son. 'Those Tchua are elder brothers of our people of Snake Clan, and so just as Hopi men must have their hair washed before they dance, so these snakes must be washed with *mohu* suds before they can be in Snake Dance.'

A few moments passed — moments of silence until the increasing blasts of heat from the sun drove the Hopi woman and her boy into the house. She settled down to work on a small plaque — an almost futile proceeding, for the trader who lived in the canyon to the east had fled from the drought and gone to the white man's town called Winslow. Then, as her thin, bony fingers began to intertwine the shreds of yucca, 'Nömsi looked up and spoke to her boy.

'It was long time ago,' she said, 'when I had only one baby, that Letaiyo got bitten by that Tchua. Our snake chief took him into kiva and did all those secret things to him. Then Letaiyo got well. But since he knew secrets of Snake Society he had to join those people. So since that time he is snake dancer when they have that dance in Mishongnovi. Since long, long ago our people have had Snake Dance, and almost always their brothers from that world below have sent rain. But our men must do right. They must make their altar right; their hearts must be full of faith, and then we shall have rain and once more we can be happy.'

For a moment faith lifted the tragic mask from her face and like a cool breeze, unexpectedly pushing its way over the heat-ridden earth, peace banished the darkness of pain from her deep-sunken eyes.

In the two kivas of the Snake and Antelope people the men, thoroughly aware of the tremendous responsibility that rested on them, had been extremely active for many days.

In the Antelope Room, an elaborate altar had been constructed on the floor, consisting of a sand painting composed of four bordering lines of color — white, red, green, and yellow for each of the directions — while inside on a white field of sprinkled meal, four zigzag lightning snakes wriggled out of four layers of clouds. These snakes and clouds were colored like the bands that edged the sacred design. At either side of the sand painting, feathered crooks stood in tiny clay pedestals, while at the right and left sides of the sand design were cotton-wrapped bundles of feathers, the sacred fetishes of the Antelope and Snake people. At one side stood a basket full of prayer sticks, while in front of the symbolic painting were four netted water jugs placed in a row with perfect ears of corn between them.

In the Snake Kiva the men who had just descended were busily engaged in the difficult task of extracting the snakes from the narrow-necked jars in which they had been kept since their capture. At one side of the kiva a bed of sand had been laid evenly on the floor, and around this, after the snakes had been released and put in sacks before them, the men sat, deeply earnest and intensely solemn with realization of the importance of their acts.

With reverential care, the Snake chief placed a large open bowl on the center of six intersecting lines, representing the paths to the four world-quarters as well as the sky home of Shotuknanguh and the black depths where Muyingwuh dwells. Then the old priest poured water into the bowl six times and added potent objects to give greater efficacy to the liquid. Then, several at a time, the snakes were plunged into the sanctified water and put out on the sand to dry.

Outside in the plaza, a *kisi*, or shaded bower of cottonwood boughs — branches with drought-dried yellow leaves — had been erected, and in this place, early in the afternoon, a sack containing all the purified snakes was hidden. Before the shelter a hole had been dug, and over this hole a thick plank had been laid.

As the sun dipped toward the west, the Antelope priests, a line of a dozen dancers, filed into the plaza. Their gray-painted bodies were zigzagged with white lines; somber colors befitting the great antiquity of their conception. Four times these priests circled about the village square, and as each man passed the *kisi*, he sprinkled meal on the wooden plank and accompanied the silent prayer with a resounding stamp on the wood that made a hollow, dull sound that might be heard by the ancestral spirits in the world below.

After that the Antelopes waited in a silent line while the Snake priests entered the plaza, and as their predecessors had done, stamped their prayer on the wooden plank. Then from the sack full of knotted, intertwisted reptiles a few at a time were handed out to the waiting dancers.

Gripping the writhing, twisting serpents firmly between their teeth or clutching them in their hands, the dancers of the Snake Society began their ritual for rain. Slowly they moved about, each snake-carrying dancer accompanied by an empty-handed partner who placed his right hand on the shoulder of the more active member of the pair.

Before the *kisi*, the Antelopes gave vocal utterance to the prayers and needs of the people. In a solemn line they sang, the pulsating rhythm of their song marked by rattles held in each hand.

As the Snake priests danced to the beat of the Antelope Song, they bent their heads backward and raised the reptiles to the dusk-darkening sky. Then, as if to draw the vitally needed rain out of the blue heights, they motioned downward with the writhing snakes, downward toward the powder-dry earth of the village square.

Completely surrounding them were the remaining men, women, and children, with an unusual number of others from the near-by towns of Shipaulovi and Shongopavi. They were not there just as spectators — the need for rain was too desperately urgent for that — but as motionless participants; for every one of them felt that life itself depended on the successful rhythmic prayer of those brown-bodied, kilted dancers. So each time the Snake priests held a clan brother aloft to the cloudless sky the hearts and minds of the people echoed the thought of the Antelope chorus as they sang their incredibly ancient prayers to the ancestral shades of the Tchamaheya and the other heroes of the wandering tribe from Tokonavi who had brought the ritual of the Snake Dance to the clans of the Hopi people.

Sikyanömsi leaned back against the wall of her sister's house, her eyes dark, leaping ovals in a motionless face. The prayers that were pounding on the earth the desperate message to the spirit world beat on her hunger-sensitized being until the sound of the feet of the Snake priests seemed to have the smashing power of the huge rocks that sometimes crashed down from the mesa's heights.

'Rain! Rain! Rain!' they called. 'There is no corn — our children die — our old people are already ghostly images ready to pass to shadow land under earth's surface. But our fathers *tchutchu pöhöknani* — they will pity us and let yellow clouds from Tokonavi tower high above our fields. In sky house of clouds lightning will flash and thunder will roar and as Shotüknanguh shoots his arrows into the clouds rain will pour out in tumbling stream. Then dry earth will drink, dying plants grow green, and water in Toriva Spring rise higher and higher. Our father from lower world will send us rain.'

As the song ended, 'Nömsi sighed with utter exhaustion, for it seemed as if every drop of blood in her body had been drained out by the flowing, pounding rhythm of their prayer. She put her hands before her eyes as if to hold back the vitality that was ebbing swiftly, as if she could no longer give of her strength to the united force that was the up-welling supplication of the people. As she did so, it was as if she held up her fingers for the gods to see, her fingers that were so skillful in weaving split yucca strands, those fingers that now had become ten gaunt bones enveloped with loose dry skin.

With one prayer ended, another began. More and more snakes were taken from the cottonwood *kisi* until there were no more left. All through the dance the priests had circled about the plaza four times with each snake that was withdrawn from the sack, and then had placed the reptile on the ground. Behind the dancers had walked the catchers, whose duty it was to pick up these temporarily discarded snakes, and as the rite reached its climax, to thrust them back into the hands of the leaping, dancing men until in their grasp they held a writhing fistful of rattlers, bullsnakes, and adders. Many of the priests gripped the reptiles between their teeth, while all the time the men who danced beside them guarded the performers from the lunging attack of the snakes. With their free left hands, warily they stroked the frantic captives with buzzard feathers in order to minimize the danger resulting from their wrath.

The red sun slid down behind the mountain home of the gods, and darkness gradually veiled the solid blue of the sky. A last song was sung — a final appeal for rain — while the Snake men, caution almost flung away, pushed their aching, undernourished bodies around and around through the still hot air of the village square, while they held up high for the gods to see the venomous clan brothers from the earth whose sinuous scaly lengths whipped about the wrists and mouths of the red-brown priests with blackened faces and white chins.

Stolidly serious, the Antelopes sang, and finally, at the conclusion of the song, their chief made on the ground a circle of finest meal and across it sprinkled lines to the six directions. After that the Snake chief made a similar design on top of the first marks of meal; then every one of the snake-holding dancers cast on the circle all the reptiles that he had clutched until every one of the snakes was piled in a quivering mass.

While the spectators pressed forward in mounting excitement, the priests rushed forward. With complete recklessness they gathered up as many serpents as they could hold, and then all rushed wildly to the north, to the west, to the south, and to the east — to the four shrines of the Snake people; there they released their captives in order that they might wriggle their way back to the underground world and convey to the gods who dwelt there the prayers of the Hopi people for rain and for the renewed gift of life.

The spectators had purified themselves by spitting toward the running priests. It was in the dimness of the dusk that Letaiyo and the other members of his order returned to Mishongnovi and drank of the bitter medicine that made them vomit away the dangerous powers that had entered into their bodies as active priests. Finally, cleansed and purified, they retired to their kiva and settled down to final ritual and prayer.

Within four days the rain must come; within four days the clouds *must* loom up and release their life-giving cargo. So it was with weary hearts high with hope that the people of the desert town waited for the answer of the gods.

Some days before the dance, one of the leaders of the Snake Society had ridden over to Shongopavi and begged the people there to do everything in their power to keep the blind man Palalökong away from the Rattlesnake ceremony. It was admitted that this would be difficult, for now no one dared to refuse a definite request from the malicious prophet who had made nearly all of them believe that he was the incarnate god of the water world underlying the earth. However, as the easily understood wishes of the Mishongnovi people were whispered from one person to another, when the time for the dance came, most of the Shongopavi people went to the other town and there hid when they saw the old man approaching.

Thus it happened that on the day of the dance the village of Shongopavi seemed deserted. The hot, thick air beat down on a silent town, devoid of motion except for the slow, shambling movement of a single burro, whose gray matted hair was insufficient to hide the bony frame of its hunger-racked body.

Palalökong crawled out of the small doorway of the solitary house in which he lived. Tap — tap — crunch, his twisted stick rapped and slithered on the rock of the village street. For a moment he stood there and listened — his body, less loathsome with dirt since the women were forced to care for him, was tense with the effort to extract sound out of the absolute stillness.

'*Aie!*' he shouted. '*Öm hinchaki?*'

Then, as his anger, ever on the surface, leaped into being at finding himself ignored, his voice grew louder and shriller, and more and more the sheer evil of his being spumed upward and became threat and curse flung about like burning hot fat spitting out of a boiling cauldron.

All through the morning he staggered about, until his fury burst into an epileptic frenzy that left him sprawled out on the ground — a meaningless mass of motionless clothes and wrinkled flesh. The burro hobbled about, searching everywhere for some stray bit of corn husk or some overlooked sprig of dried-out plant.

The sun slowly slid along its prescribed arc, and still the old man lay in the heat and dust of the desert day. Then, as late afternoon approached, sound began to creep through space; sound from the east; sound that was the chanted prayer of men, faint and indistinguishable.

The burro poked his way about and then discovered the old man. The gray velvet nose of the animal nudged the still figure inquiringly until it seemed to infect the aged form with motion, for first a hand began to twitch, then a leg to move, until, after many efforts, the half-unconscious man stood on his feet and then, clutching the burro, lifted himself up on the animal's back.

Gradually thought seeped into his wreck of a mind, and with it fear. He had been left alone — his power was gone, for without others to serve him he would die. The significance of the silence made him think more sanely than he had been able to do for months past. He was alone — there was no one there — no one to feed him — no one to find water — there was no one there but the ever-present Massauh, Skeleton Man and God of the Dead.

Suddenly the faint sound of the distant song darted into and captured the old man's thought. Song! The song of dancing men! The song of Antelope priests chanting for rain! And if rain came? If rain came, then even if the people returned, his power was gone and the young men would jeer at him and throw him down in the filth and mud and let him lie there to starve.

So his fear of the result of rain grew to conviction that somehow he must make his way to Mishongnovi — somehow he must counteract the power of those snake-clutching men, who otherwise might send effective prayer through to the gods who control the rain.

First he must find his stick and learn in just what part of the village he was. Holding tight to the burro with one hand, he slid to the ground and groped about until he found his cane. Then, once more he mounted the thin, gray animal, and whacking it with his stick forced it to move about. Then he kept jabbing the air until he found the solid substance of a wall. Carefully he explored its surface until he had identified it as the Wuwuchim Kiva. Then, keeping the continuous sound of the Antelope priests steadily to the right of him, he forced the burro to trot along until he felt a downward incline in the trail. Testing the correctness of his position, he felt for and found a solid wall of rock on his left. Then abruptly the burro turned, but Palalökong knew that it was following the winding trail to the base of the mesa.

Down they went, right and left, past the ruins of the ancient town that had been abandoned centuries before. Then all at once the sound of distant song ceased.

In complete dismay, the old man halted the burro. If the dance were over, he could never be guided by its sound across the dunes and washes that separate the east and west towns of the middle mesa.

Again fear twisted his heart and petulant whimpering crept through his lips, until once more the Antelope priests, in far-off Mishongnovi, all unconsciously gave, by their singing, a compass to the hated blind man with which to guide him across the miles of sand. Again anger rooted out fear, and, beating the offenseless burro savagely with his stick, Palalökong forced it to trot eastward. Heading into the sound of song, he guided the animal until finally the voices of the chorus came from high above him and, as he climbed the trail, for the first time he heard the rhythmic pounding of the Snake priests, earnestly beseeching their clan ancestors for clouds and rain. Then from the height of Mishongnovi there was complete and lasting silence.

Below the town there is a broad ledge more than half-way up the mesa, and there, without sound to guide him, Palalökong found himself lost. At first he tried to let the burro take his own trail, but that proved to be home-ward and down the slope to the west. So impatiently the old man wheeled the animal about and tried again and again to find the beginning of the passage upward. Finally he noticed that the burro's feet were sinking into soft sand, so he rode to the left, keeping the animal always in the sand, until he came to the place where the diagonal trail cuts through a dune under the village's southern rim and ascends steeply to the town itself.

'Nömsi, 'Yeshva, and the girls with old Makya, whose hair was now as white as the clouds that stayed away, were just about to enter their house when over the sand crest before them they saw the weird figure of the blind Palalökong riding toward them.

Despair swept over Sikyanömsi like a wave of pain. The hope that had winged its way higher and higher with each song of the Antelopes and each pounded beat of the Snake men dropped with the suddenness of a dead eagle falling from the sky.

With a face devoid of expression, she stood before her home while Palalökong, sensing the presence of people, rode up to her and demanded food.

'*Wi, ancha'ai,*' she said. '*Yungya'ai* — you can come in ——' She sighed and opened the door.

XVII. WHEN EARTH DIES, FAITH CLIMBS TO THE STARS

WORD spread quickly through the village and to the kiva, where the men were assembled, that the blind Palalökong had succeeded in making his way over the winding trail to Mishongnovi. If earlier anyone had doubted the superhuman nature of the aged madman, now in the face of his seemingly miraculous arrival skepticism became impossible.

To the men of the Snake Society the blow hit hardest. For days they had worked ceaselessly, buoyant with hope in the power and ultimate outcome of their ancient clan ritual. All through the dance they had poured out their desperate need in vocal prayer to the gods; every man of them had danced with his entire being charged with faith that rain would come within four days; and now the evil power of the blind man stood like a wall of rock, shutting out all hope and leaving them bowed with the despair of knowing the utter futility of their action to direct the power of the gods.

Letaiyo, all his senses numb with the shock of murdered hope, fumbled his way up the ladder and then lurched heavily through the darkness to the door of his home. Through the small windows an unusual amount of light shone, and as he entered the room he saw squatting before him the slobbering figure of Palalökong, his hands in a bowl of stew and his face slimy with grease and corn. The food that would have sufficed for the family need for days was being devoured or flung about the floor by the blind man, who seemed to have taken complete possession of the home.

Grimly Letaiyo looked at his wife, whose face was as devoid of expression as the mud walls of the house. At one side of the room Kwayeshva sat, twisting a piece of leather without aim or purpose. His sisters leaned against the wall near him and stared, almost without moving their eyelids, at the old man, whose coming was so tragic for them all. Against another wall lay the comatose figure of Sowüchti, for whom the life trail was ending. A few more hours — perhaps days — and then, after hovering about for a short time, her spirit would pass to the skeleton world, where the substance of food was neither known nor needed.

Palalökong, finding that there was no more food, grumbled a bit about its scantiness and then demanded a sheepskin to lie on. Soon he was stretched out on a thick white fur, where almost immediately he fell asleep. From time to time his body twitched as he lay there, and occasionally his talon-tapered hands clawed suggestively at the air, as if even in his dreams he was clutching at the people he was able to dominate through fear.

For a long time 'Nömsi and her family sat there in silence. Finally she put her hands before her eyes as if to shut out the picture of the old man. Letaiyo arose and walked over to her. Tenderly he touched her with his fingers, and as he did so 'Nömsi put her hands in his and looked up at him with an expression which showed devotion to the father of her children, trying to let hope rise upward from the nadir of despair.

'What can we do?' she asked in a voice that was thin and colorless.

Letaiyo sighed. For some moments he stared intently into the rafters, the still fixity of his expression a mask for the frantic thoughts that were trying to plod through the storm of fear and desperate worry that clouded his mind. Finally he turned to his wife.

'If this Palalökong stays here, we shall all starve,' he said. For some minutes more he searched vainly for some kind of escape from the intolerable situation which the blind man's coming had created. 'Maybe we should go away,' he suggested at last; 'maybe — we should go to Hano.'

'Nömsi nodded her approval of the plan, but then as her mind began to catch at such a thought, she motioned toward the still body of her mother.

'Sowüchti is too near Maski. While she lives, I must stay here. Then, when she goes to that spirit world, maybe we can go to Hano — our friends will be glad to see us there.'

The rugged strength that had carried 'Nömsi's mother to great age had fought the privation of drought; but her once fat, round little form had shrunk and withered until it had become seemingly just a bewildered, inquiring pair of deep-sunken black eyes, peering about out of a loose, sagging mass of wrinkles. Occasionally her dulled understanding would make her whimper like a child when food was denied her; but for the greater part of the time she lay quiet, in stoic resignation or in the calm peace of the sleep that is the dawn of death.

For four days she clung to the world that up to now had been, for the greater part, a joyous one; then early in the afternoon, like a feather whose slight movement has ceased, her body became completely still.

It was Kwayeshva who first noticed that his grandmother had died, and the realization of the fact struck him like the sudden blast of a sandstorm. Quick thoughts from his youth darted before him of the woman who had carried him on her back as a child; of the bowlegged figure that had trudged up and down the long trail from Toriva; of the kindly, autocratic old woman who had made him cut wood or hunt for game. Now, in four days, her spirit would float over the cliff that rises upward from the lower realm. As her life had been a kindly one, free from evildoing, she would be able to make her way to the skeleton world without having to struggle through the thick masses of cactus that always impede the path of the unworthy. Soon her spirit would descend to the stone houses of Maski, and there she would enter into her new abode by climbing down a ladder of sunflower stalks.

Sorrowfully the women washed the thin gray hair of their aged relative, and then rubbed a few grains of corn into her scalp. Solemnly an old man who had been her father's kinsman tied prayer sticks to her forehead so that her wrinkled face was covered by the eagle plumes. Then a *potavi*, which symbolized her life trail, was laid on her body so that its breast feather was placed on her mouth and its cotton length reached over her body to her navel. On top of her head was fastened the white breast feather that would carry her to the spirit world.

In the rocky graveyard outside of the town, a round pit was dug, and after *piki* and dried meat had been placed on Sowüchti's breast and her entire body, dressed in her finest clothes, had been wrapped in a blanket with an opening provided for the outward journey of her soul, her still form was placed in the grave in sitting position, with her face toward the rising sun. Beside her were a jug of water — an infinitely precious gift to the departed — and a small bit of food, of which her soul might inhale the essence and thus gain sufficient strength to reach the lower world.

On returning to the village, the men stopped four times, and on each occasion made four parallel marks on the ground with sacred meal in order that the ghostly spirit of the deceased might never return.

Then a thoroughly weary Sikyanömsi, four days after her mother's death, replastered the house as a rite of purification. The walls and the floor were completely coated with thin adobe mud, although poor 'Nömsi shivered with fear as she realized what a large amount of their tiny reserve of water was being used for this purpose.

All through these days, when sorrow and a constant labor had taxed her strength to the utmost, Sikyanömsi had been forced to endure the presence and the ceaseless cursing of Palalökong, who had stayed all the time in or near the house and at all hours demanded food and received it, regardless of the meagerness of the supply.

At first, after his sudden arrival, some of the younger

men of Mishongnovi had whispered among themselves that they ought to kill the madman whom they hated so intensely; but the village chiefs had heard of the plan, and, in the genuineness of their fear, they had convinced the youths that some even more horrible calamity would overtake them if they executed such a deed.

The meeting that had taken place in a kiva four days after the Snake Dance had been a heartless affair. There was no need to probe into the conduct of the various participants to see if individual fault had marred the efficacy of the ritual. It was too obvious that the mighty wrath of the Plumed Serpent, who had come to live among them as Palalökong, the blind man, was entirely responsible for the failure of the rite.

Some hope was revived when the men of Shongopavi danced and, freed from the presence of the old madman, entered into their ceremony with an upward surge of faith. Still, all through the final hours of that day the people of Mishongnovi cowered in fear of the curses that Palalökong had flung about as he heard the distant sound of song floating across the desert from his former home.

All through the late afternoon, while the dance was in progress, he had stood on the west side of the village, facing Shongopavi, and had mumbled or shrieked that the rain would not come because he, Palalökong, controlled all the water of the earth and he had told it to stay away from the Hopi land.

As night fell, one of his frequent fits had seized him and tumbled him into a twitching heat on the hot dust at the head of the sand trail to Toriva. There he had lain for hours while, in the light of a rising and infinitely revealing moon, for a long time his arms and legs had kicked and jerked about, while nearly all the people of the town had stood in a silent circle, watching yet fearing acutely this obvious manifestation of the old man's unearthly power. Then gradually they had retreated to their homes, and through the remaining night hours the unconscious Palalökong lay there where he had fallen.

Early in the morning, before the sun had thrust its yellow hues into the white light of its first coming, suddenly the dreaded old man had aroused the village with ear-splitting shrieks and howls, wilder and infinitely more horrible than anything the people had heard before. As many of them rushed out-of-doors in a panic, they saw him standing near the Snake Kiva, his face smeared with clotted blood, while his body and his clothing were coated with mingled dust and crimson stain.

His rage seemed to be colored with extreme pain, and as his cries mounted like the shrilling of a wounded dog, blood bubbled and spilled out of his mouth. Out of all the fury that was flung from his black and bloody form, like flashes from a thundercloud, one fact had instantly penetrated the consciousness of every person in the crowd: the fact that all his shrieks and wailings were meaningless, tumbled, jumbled sounds without the recognizable form of speech, that not one single word emerged from the lips that dribbled blood.

Each ray of the sun that day was like a red-hot arrow point darting from the heights at all the living things that dared to exist on the seared surface of the earth, and all through the day Palalökong clawed at his bleeding mouth and flung himself about from house to house screaming at the people and staining the floors, until finally, before Sikyanömsi's hearth, with a sigh that was the faintest echo of his earlier howls, he slipped into the silence and immobility of exhausted sleep.

Ever since Sowüchti's death Letaiyo and his family had been planning and preparing to leave for the Tewa town to the east. Their meager supply of corn had been bundled together and tied up in a blanket; likewise a pile of dried meat — the remains of the last burro sacrificed to necessity — and a few personal possessions were added; and that night they left their house to the sole occupancy of the unconscious blind man, who unaccountably seemed to have become dumb as well.

Night drew its black coolness over the earth that had been so cruelly violated by the sun's power. The moon tilted its curved form in slow, untroubled ascent as five thin figures marched down the sandy trail and on past the mighty shaft of rock, the 'one of two still standing' that had given Mishongnovi its name.

The rise and fall of a moon-silvered desert, patterned here and there with shadow, was an outstretched land vibrant with promise, and peaceful from the stroking movement of the night-cooled breeze, while over its dunes and eroded washes slowly plodded ahead five fugitives from the uncompromising forces of their arid world.

The soft sand, uncemented by any trace of moisture, yielded to the pressure of their moccasined feet as if it had been a mire. Here and there dead desert shrubs, brittle as ancient bones, snapped as they were trodden down. Under the feet of the travelers the world was a lifeless plain, but above them the stars skipped and danced in a perfect frenzy of excited animation, and the rising arc of the moon glowed placidly and contentedly, like a mother watching the antics of her exuberant young.

The shadows crawled away from the open desert and crouched in the deep canyon, behind the pinnacles of rock that lifted their solid substance high above the crumbling grit and shattered stone below.

Through alternate darkness and glistening light, Letaiyo and his family pushed their way eastward, through sand that gripped at their tired feet as if to hold them, and over rocky ledges that were hard, firm, unyielding. Mile after mile moved from before them to the western background, while ahead the eastern mesa, like a giant wedge, cut through the arid waste and, as they approached, loomed higher and higher in almost insolent desolation, in apparent defiance of desert drought, and in utter indifference to the animation of sky-flecked light.

As they came near, the massive wall blotted out half of the stars as it stretched its seemingly immutable substance across the sky. Then, as the Hopi family climbed higher, all at once the ageless rock trembled as with sudden weakness and 'Nömsi clung to her husband as some of the mass, dried beyond ability to adhere to the cliff, suddenly smashed its thundering way downward, and then scattered its substance among the stones that similarly had fallen in the ages of the past. The sound roared and rolled through the canyon, and was followed by a smooth silence that in turn was gashed by the sharp edge of a coyote's howl.

Quietly the five ascended a long sand slope, and then near the Isva Spring they all stretched out for an hour's sleep. High above them the three villages, Walpi, Sitchumovi, and Hano, made irregular outline against the festive sky. Below, the sand on which they laid their tired bodies was surface-cooled, but underneath the dry grains were throbbing with the stored heat that had been forced upon the earth during the long, cloudless day.

For Letaiyo the feverish thoughts that could not be ignored were like a warring army stalking his weary brain, prodding its aching substance with spear-points of acute worry, and brandishing clubs with ominous foreboding that threatened to crash downward — downward — to crush and to kill.

Yet, he thought, life in all its essence was so simple. It depended for its continuance on bits of food and a little water. Food which ordinarily grew all about them — desert plants and cultivated corn, as well as prairie dogs, rabbits, or once in a while much larger game. Then, too, water, such as had welled upward in cool abundance in the Toriva, Isva, and other springs — water that was deep and clear as long as rain fell from time to time. But when the springs dried up and the plants withered, and the wild life in the desert fled to the distant heights or became stench-laden food for the clawing birds, then life ceased for man as well — and all for lack of rain. So, therefore, he reflected, rain was life — rain was joy — rain was freedom. And rain came when the gods so willed.

And what caused the gods to will it? Faith — industry — clean hearts and minds; for so he had been taught. Faith as expressed in ceremony; industry to prove their worthiness, and their willingness to do all they could to help themselves; clean hearts and minds to stand guard in protection of the home.

So, as Letaiyo pondered these things, there crystallized in him the conviction that, instead of yielding to despair or losing faith in the power of the gods because the rain had been withheld, from then on life must be lived in greater purity of body and mind; in increased industry and more deeply rugged faith; that even if death were drawing the last breath from his body, still he must keep faith with the chief gods who had fathered him and the people of his clan, and in long-gone days had laid down the lasting laws for the people.

There had been much wrongdoing by certain ones he knew, and might it not be possible that just as the breaking of the stalks of the kiva-grown green beans in the Powamuya winter ritual by just one single man meant crop failure for them all, so the evil selfish doings of any individual might likewise bring about the condemnation and the wiping-out of an entire mighty tribe?

Overhead, the stars seemed to weary of their frolic, and grew quieter and more subdued until all but the more sprightly ones, like dulling coals on the hearth, shed their gleam and became as one with the slowly graying sky.

Not long afterward, in the yellow haze of second dawn, Sikyanömsi stirred her cramped, her age-marked, aching body, and brushing away the dreams that had haunted her hour of sleep arose and woke her children. Then she turned and looked at her man. He lay with his head against a stone; even though his eyes were closed, he seemed to be looking upward, and 'Nömsi noted with wonder that the wrinkles which had gripped his face for the months that had just passed were now somewhat smooth, as if by some inner, quiet tone, by the power of some new-found peace. Strangely strengthened likewise, 'Nömsi touched her husband, almost timidly, with her fingertips. As he awoke he smiled, and in his smile the Hopi woman felt the strength of faith that had quietly brushed away despair.

Slowly they trudged up the winding trail to Hano and to the home of their Tewa friends. At the weather-beaten door they paused, and slowly the man rapped. From within came invitation and response.

'*Yungya'ai*,' was called.

Letaiyo opened the door and stood there before Polakka and his wife. 'We have come,' he announced, as the others entered too.

Knowing nothing of the reason, the Tewa man replied, '*Ancha'ai*, Letaiyo. It is well.'

XVIII. PACHAVA, WHEN THE GODS GO MAD

ALL through the day the two men talked: talked of the strange arrival of Palalökong in Mishongnovi; talked of the unbearable fact of his coming to live at 'Nömsi's house; of his devouring the carefully hoarded food; of the weird manner in which the blind man had become speechless. Finally they talked about the conviction that had brought peace and strength to Letaiyo: the conviction that faith, industry, and purity were the three essential ways of living if they were to win the favor and aid of the gods.

To this last belief Polakka gave the full support of his approval.

'It is right,' he declared. 'We must live as our fathers told us to. Those boys in Walpi, they are bad. They make big fun over our old chief and say he is no good — that he is Walpi slave. Then they do bad things to our girls, and some Tewa boys are just as bad. They think maybe it is smart to be like those Walpi men, so they say mean things to our old people.

'But maybe if our Tewa and Hopi men try hard to live right and make their Katchinas come and dance, then our gods will be sorry that we have no rain. But if we all are bad like those Walpi boys, then our Katchinas will be mad and they will make us die.

'This year all our people will be busy because our

boys are to be in Wuwuchim ceremony. We try to forget we are mad at Walpi people because, when we have that big Wuwuchim, our men of all three villages must take part together. Maybe when Pachava comes, and our Hopi Mong Katchinas visit us, then those clouds will all be sorry that they stayed away so long and they will come to our fields and make our corn grow high and our springs deep with clear water.

'My boy, Mahle, he will be in Wuwuchim this year, and his godfather will take him down to our spring and make him bathe when water is all ice.'

A puzzled look crept into the Tewa man's eyes. 'But still, we have no water in that spring,' he remembered. 'Maybe there will be no ice then for our boys to take bath in as our fathers told us they should do.'

He paused in genuine bewilderment. 'That is bad,' he declared. 'Maybe if those boys can't take those baths in snow and ice their Katchinas won't be able to make that rain come.'

'We still have some little bit of water,' Letaiyo said, 'and maybe those boys can bathe in that. Maybe just enough to make a few drops fall on each one who is to dance.' Then, expressing his anxiety over the situation in the town to which he had been forced to come, he asked, 'Where do Tewa people get their water now?'

'Hopoko,' answered Polakka, pointing toward the east. 'There is little bit by Sikyatki, and some more where that Bahana had his house. We still have some food, maybe enough to eat until spring comes. If our Katchinas that come in Pachava bring us good rain, then we shall be all right.'

Weeks and months passed, and the heat waves that had arisen dizzily from the earth ceased to shimmer; instead, fierce winds from the north drove cold air against the rock wall of the mesa and the stone and adobe houses that surmounted it.

In all the villages the women had performed their great annual dances and the men and boys had wrestled frantically for baskets tossed toward them by the participants. Still the women were no more successful in drawing the rain clouds to Hopi than the men had been, for day after day passed without a trace of white film streaking the blue vastness of the sky. The springs at Sikyatki and where 'the Bahana lived' were used up, and long expeditions had to be made to the remote water-holes and the precious liquid doled out bit by bit to each family.

A slight flurry of snow one day, lasting for an hour, sent the people out in frenzied excitement, to scoup up every particle of the fluffy substance so that it might be stored. Then, when the sun came out again and rapidly melted and made away with the remaining snow, each family found they had secured perhaps a week's supply of water and a prodigious amount of cheer from the totally unexpected event.

Some of this was used for the Wuwuchim initiation that began a few days later and continued for many days.

Mahle had heard that it was a severe test of his manhood that lay before him, and neither he nor any of the other boys knew just exactly what the ordeal was to be. Of course baring his body to the cold of snow, ice, and winter wind was merely a slightly emphasized repetition of an experience to which he had been accustomed from childhood. The long races, too, of five, ten, or twenty miles were nothing unusual. Perhaps, though, the fact that they had been able to eat so little food for so many months would mean that his thin body would not be able to endure the strain. He discussed the matter with Kwayeshva, and they agreed that Mahle undoubtedly was in for a strenuous time.

It all started with the kindling of a new fire in one of the kivas — a flame that was carried to each of the other underground rooms that in them likewise a new cycle of life should be commenced. Sixteen days of ceremony followed — days in which hunger-fevered men and women surrendered their treasured bits of food in order that the ceremony of the Wuwuchim might be conducted properly. In each of four kivas altars were constructed by the Alwimi, the Towimi, the Wuwuchimwimi, and the Kwanwimi, the four ceremonial groups to one of which every Hopi man must belong on reaching manhood. There the gods of the north, the west, the south, and the east were honored, as well as the deity of the nadir.

Then days of dancing followed; days when the novices begged for food from the women of the three towns, food that was given even though it meant hunger-racked days and famished nights for the donors. Above it all the wooden figure of Talatömsi, the Goddess of the Dawn, hovered like a patron saint.

To every man, woman, boy, and girl the thought hung over each of their heads, as omnipresent as the cloudless sky, that all the other ceremonies of the Hopi had failed to bring rain, and that now the supreme ritual was being performed — that for three months all personal jealousies and dislikes must be put away. That Walpi and Hano must dance or plant prayer plumes together; and that all thought, all action must be concentrated on the continuous chain of ceremonies that would end with the Pachava when more than a hundred Katchinas would appear — Katchinas that were the mightiest of all the Hopi gods and whose favor could, without question, bring rain to sink gently into the dust-swirling fields and transform them from mocking stretches of brown waste to row upon row of green-sheaved prosperity.

The sixteen days of Wuwuchim having ended, an exhausted, sleep-craving Mahle — on whom had been bestowed a new name — flung himself on a sheepskin before his mother's hearth and slept for two risings of the sun.

Soon after that Auhalani, the great god of the Patki people, made his appearance with the blue and yellow corn girls, and in the chief kiva a great bank of corn was made into an altar — corn ears that were perfect specimens, jealously saved by each Hopi family in order that they might be sanctified by use in the kiva ritual, and then used in the spring as the seed corn that would be planted in a wet, moist earth and there in time grow to maturity and yield an abundant harvest.

In the kiva the Kwataka, the Bird Man, who symbolized the sky, postured amorously before a blossom-petaled virgin and danced with her until the petals of her purity had fallen to the ground. Then the venerable sun Katchina Ahöla made his annual visit to the kivas and homes of the people and placed on them his mark of protection. The Powamuya Katchinas danced in the firelit darkness, and finally the day of Pachava dawned with a tumult of ceremony that turned the three towns of the eastern mesa into a dazzling, color-flashing mass of gods and men, with the former in the great majority.

Still, for all the festive glory of the scene, it was a tense, hunger-muted crowd that saw the black-and-white-striped Shoyongeva come into the village at sunrise, thus completing a fourfold circuit of the mesa that had started in the dead of night. No happy smiles or trace of laughter touched the gray-brown faces of the people as He'eheh, the Warrior Maiden, came singing from the Sun Shrine at Kowawai'ima and then, starting in Hano, went from kiva to kiva in all three of the eastern villages. None of the usual gasps of delight or sparkling eyes greeted the vast number of Katchinas that poured out of kiva after kiva as soon as the goddess had walked four times about each sky hole.

Massauh, dreaded god of the skeleton world, was there, marching about with a huge drum. Shotöknanguh the cloud-symboled deity of the sky, strode from town to town in colorful splendor. Wupamu Katchinas, with masks like the sun, lashed about at those who ventured to obstruct their way. Warrior gods, such as Sikya'hote, stalked through the streets, trailing their eagle-tail head-dresses that hung from their blue, star-patterned masks down to the frozen ground.

Pongkwiyo and her daughter, with 'Nömsi and the three girls from Mishongnovi, sat blanket-wrapped before the house of a relative in the Hano square. All their men were in the dance. Polakka had become a fierce owl, a fighter who hooted as he marched about and who was accompanied by two owlets, a boy and a girl, who trotted after him from Hano to Walpi and back again. The small sons of Pongkwiyo's sisters were impersonating these little birds, and the nearest approach to a smile that touched the dull mask of Sikyanömsi's face was when this trio passed in front of them.

Butterfly Girl, though, was quite excited because she was waiting to see her friend 'Yeshva, who had decided to take part with another boy in a double performance. The latter was to be a Koyemsi who had lassoed a growling Wupamu Katchina, which yucca-brandishing sun god was of course Kwayeshva himself. It was when He'eheh made her third visit to the kiva in the Hano square that the pair climbed up the ladder from the dark interior and Wupamu Katchinas peered about and uttered angry, deep-throated growls.

To the boys, the pleasure that normally they would have taken in their part in the masked ritual was more than tempered by their extreme weariness. Their young bodies had been deprived of more than half-handfuls of food for so long that the rigor of nights of kiva practice and ceremony, which for days had robbed them of sleep, had drained out what remaining strength was left to them. Almost listlessly they charged about here and there, Wupamu Katchina assuming a continuous air of ferocity, and the Mudhead holding him in check or occasionally protecting himself with buzzard feathers from the angry god's wrath. The cold clawed at their nearly nude bodies, the wind whipped and cut as they passed back and forth from Hano to Walpi, two of more than a hundred gods who had been famished men, working ceaselessly, day and night, to prove to the supreme beings that their faith and industry were sufficient to justify the coming of the rain.

Other men had taken the parts of clowns and funmakers. But their antics, that ordinarily would have been hailed with shouts of joy-impelled laughter, now were greeted with thin smiles or occasionally a giggle that contained no trace of merriment, but was a sudden slipping of the grip that had clung to self-control by sheer power of will.

As the brilliant forms marched or danced before her, 'Nömsi for some time ceased to see them. Her eyes were lifted to the cold cobalt mass of the sky. There were no birds to streak across its length and breadth; nothing but a rising and falling sun. Yet surely now, after all their months of ceremony, the Fathers of the four world-quarters would take pity on them and build cloud houses along the paths in the sky. Surely the snow, like stars dropping gaily from above, would spread its smooth protectiveness over the lifeless nudity of the earth.

As if it had been created by her thought, a tiny ball of white pushed itself into sight from behind the barren cones of Növatukyaovi. It was just a minute cloud, quite too immature to bear rain, but still it was a definite reality that might be nurtured by winging hope and prayer; it was a focal point on which could be concentrated all the thought and despair that had welled upward from suffering to realization.

For several weeks past, Sikyanömsi had been aware of a woman living near the home of Pongkwiyo, who had plodded about as if in a continual daze. Her lips had constantly been forming the syllables of soundless words and her hands had become as rigid as the dried cornstalks of their desert fields. All at once the Mishongnovi woman noticed that this oddly behaving neighbor was standing near her and that she too was staring intently at the cloud that was like a solitary cotton boll in the sky.

Her eyes were unwinking; then her skin-dried lips began to twitch, and all at once a weird smile, almost of inner ecstasy, flushed her being. As if drawn by a magnet, she moved forward toward a house and then, without using her hands, walked up a ladder and stood for some time motionless on the roof with her hands extended before her, staring fixedly at the small spot of white that hung in the western sky. Finally her lips began to quiver and presently words began tumbling from her like splashing water bounding over a dam.

'Nömsi, Pongkwiyo, and the girls, as well as many other women, followed after, sensing in her the eeriness of one whose mind has suddenly come into contact with the world of outer power. Quietly they stood below while the woman stepped to the very edge of the roof and, still staring with rigid eyes at the cloud, drew herself up to the extreme limit of her height. Then in gaunt silhouette against the sky her face suddenly changed to a tender expression of maternity. Her hands relaxed and made caressing motions as if she were cradling and giving her strength to an invisible child.

'Little white cloud' — her voice was a mere murmur — 'come lie in my arms, *puva*, *puva*. Here you shall sleep; here you shall grow. Grow to be strong, my cloud; grow to bear rain. Then there tall rain shall stand; stand like great forest pines, sturdy and strong. Then there that rain shall walk, striding high sky. Rain from our yellow north; rain from white east. Rain from that red of south; rain from blue west. Then all our barren land will sing and shout its joy. Corn plants will rise with song; corn plants, corn boys and girls. Waving their tasseled heads, swelling with seed. Making our people strong; making our children dance.

'White cloud, sleep on my breast, *puva* be strong.'

For a moment she reached her arms out as if to enfold the whole universe; then, with a flash of light in her eyes as if darkness had been cleft for her, she toppled forward to the cold, hard earth below.

Silently, stirred to their innermost being, Sikyanömsi and the other women carried her crushed, still form to her home and laid her down on a sheepskin. Outside the gods marched about in solemn ritual, and above a tiny cloud dared its way across the infinite distance of the blue, then wearied and allowed its substance to be absorbed by the sun that stood gleaming down from the very zenith.

Not long after, 'Nömsi went back to her new home. She felt that she must think in solitude, for she was crushed by the solid weight of the thoughts that had massed together, by the seeming significance of the woman's strange union with the powers of the infinite heights. Could it be prophecy that the rain would be born to them by the little cloud? No; for now that small tuft of white had vanished. Perhaps, though, it had disappeared into the beyond with the soul of the woman who had cradled it so tenderly in her thought. Then it might be that in some distant world it would be nourished and strengthened, and would finally return in full-billowing maturity to spread its life-giving essence over the Hopi land.

So in 'Nömsi's heart conviction glowed like a dancing flame that no matter whether the rain came now or not, some day that round, white cloud would roll over the desert sands and restore the joy and health that had been torn away from them these many months. As she went out-of-doors once more there was a sureness in her stride, a clearness in her eye, that made those she passed turn to look at her in wonder.

Straight through Sitchumovi she walked over the narrow rock trail to Walpi, to the western limits of the mesa. For a short time she stood there looking toward Növatükyaovi, and it seemed to her that in the clear distance of the west she could see a land of flowing water and abundant harvest through the blue haze above the upthrust cones of the sacred mountains.

A sudden, shrill cry made her turn in startled surprise. Then she smiled as she saw the black-masked figure of the Warrior Goddess, He'eheh, brandishing a mountain-lion quiver about her head while she stood on the housetop from which the Cha'akmongwi makes his announcement. Of course, she remembered, it was time now for the gods 'to go mad,' so she must hurry back to Pongkwiyo's house or she would be whipped by the Ichivuh Katchinas, those angry ones that were already driving all the women and children into the houses so that they could not see the things that were about to take place in the open parts of the towns.

Scurrying along, she eluded the stinging whips of

the gods, who hooted furiously at her as she ran through Walpi. Over the rocks and through the long streets of Sitchumovi she hastened, while the Katchinas grew angrier and angrier to see anyone still out-of-doors. As she entered Hano, she noticed her own Kwayeshva as Wupamu Katchina, dashing after one old soul, who was toddling as fast as her ancient legs would carry her toward the house that would afford her refuge from the anger of the gods who for three hours would guard the streets.

Inside, windows were covered with blankets and the children were warned that under no circumstances must they make any attempt to peep out, even if they could find a crack or a chink that was not stuffed up with rags.

In the Tewa kiva that clung to the rocky side of the mesa not far from Pongkwiyo's house, Kwayeshva and Mahle either were watching the busy scene or taking part in it. 'Yeshva's duties kept him out-of-doors for the greater part of the time, policing the deserted towns; but occasionally his intense curiosity and absorbing interest caused him to dash into the kiva to see how Mahle was getting along or to watch the old men who were so actively engaged in the secret preparation for the most sacred, potent rite in all Hopi masked ceremonialism.

In the center of the floor a great cone of cedar bark was being erected on a flat tray. Bean plants, tall, wax-like, and translucently yellow-green, were pulled up carefully by the roots — a delicate operation, considering that a single broken stalk might nullify the power of the entire ceremony. As in the Powamuya, they had been grown in individual pots and boxes and huge quantities of them were now in readiness.

Carefully the chiefs wrapped bunches of them together with yucca strands and then fastened to these thin straight wooden sticks. This being done, each bundle was gently thrust into the cedar cone so that when all the sprouts had been inserted into its tapering shell, the whole structure resembled a huge mass of growing plants.

Mahle and one other boy had been the members of that kiva to undergo the rigors of the Wuwuchim initiation. Therefore they were to be masked as particularly important Katchinas — Pong Katchinas, green-and-white snow gods such as had once danced to Kwayeshva's song. And as these mighty deities they were to be privileged to carry the tray and cone of living plants in the great procession that would take place as soon as all was in readiness.

Then, as the winter sun hung halfway down the western sky, the narrow ledge of rock that is the Katchinki, or house of the masked deities, below the southeast trail into Walpi, was covered with a solid mass of a hundred and fifty men — pairs from each kiva in the three towns as well as the vast number that had roamed about through the morning. Feathered head-dresses crushed against wooden cloud-frames; angry monsters rubbed elbows with radiant star or sun gods. Animals with tapering horns crowded the birds with pointed bills into the ice-cold sides of the rocky wall. Here and there young girls in their early maturity looked excited and eager as they prepared to wear masks for the one and only time in their lives, and to act as assistants to the carriers who were to bear the harvest-symbolizing cones of secretly grown beans.

Mahle, standing guard over his precious plants, gazed in wonder at the color-shimmering scene about him. Forgotten was his hunger, his lassitude of the morning, for he felt a very surge of power emanating from the thickly packed crowd of mighty beings who had come from the most ancient of days to take possession, for a time, of the bodies of men, and to unite in fighting the deadly force that was crumbling the earth and all forms of life into the dry powder of death.

Below him, far down the sheer sides of the mesa wall, were pile upon pile of mammoth rocks, straight-edged as if they had been broken by mighty hands and then tossed in a heap like chips of wood.

Westward, the sun slid along its course of blue, grim as a stern father who will not be moved by appeal.

Then down the rock steps from above, led by quiet-faced, earnest priests, came the mightiest of the mighty gods, Aototo, chief divinity of the Kokop Clan. Likewise in line were Angwusnasumtaka, the Crow-Winged Mother of the flogging gods, followed by her hooting, whip-swishing sons. Quietly they took their places at the head of the procession that formed on the narrow ledge; then, followed by ten pairs of plant-bearing gods aided by their sister deities, up the trail they went.

The dozens of Katchinas that had appeared in the morning kept close to the carriers from their own kivas, and as they climbed the steps of stone each one hooted, shrilled, or growled until the desert waste echoed with the blended, eery sound. From the houses of the three towns people were hurrying to reach the Walpi square before the final rites began. Hope and faith were pushing suddenly through the tired, drawn faces. Hands that had hung listlessly at the sides of their bodies began to move in eager accompaniment to speech, while the eyes that had been dulled by want and pain once more flashed with traces of the joy that had given their name to the 'happy people,' the Hopituh Shinimuh.

Near the strange cone of rock that rises miraculously from the level floor of the Walpi square, 'Nömsi, her Tewa friend, and their girls stood, packed tightly together by the pressure of the tense, eager crowd, who saw in the approaching ceremony the certain release from the horror and destruction of drought and slow starvation.

Slowly and with infinite dignity, the priests made marks, ten in all, on the ground before them. On each of these the white-robed Aototo sprinkled cloud and rain symbols with finest meal. Then on these god-made signs the ten living masses of slim green growth were laid, in order that, as the rain and cloud marks were united with the symbols of life sustained by food, the clouds would loose their stored-up moisture and the union of the mother earth and the male power of the sky result in life — life abundant — life for the soul as well as life for the famine-racked bodies of the people of the desert land.

Four times the designs were resprinkled by the cloud-white god. Four times the product of the earth was placed upon them. Then a solemn priest plucked from each pile the topmost bunch of sprouts, and after prying up the flat rock that conceals the shrine, the *sipapuni* of ancestral emergence, the plants were carefully placed inside as an offering to the spirits of the shadow land.

The slow deliberation of the priestly acts was then whipped into sudden speed as a shouting voice called to the women to cover the heads of their boys and girls. Hastily blankets were folded over wriggling heads; eyes that were too young to see were hidden in the folds of blue-black skirts, while with a whoop of joy ten men, two from the chief kiva and one from each of the others, rushed toward the sprouted beans, gathered them up with a sudden, possessive swoop, and then dashed each to the dark concealment of his kiva.

The hundred gods of the morning ritual also leaped away, tilting their masks back over their heads so that the speed of their departure might not send them crashing into some house or rock.

After that the children, released from the smothering folds of opaque cloth, looked about in wonderment, for the Walpi square that had been a teeming mass of vivid color had become a place of quiet, calm where the carrier and greatest gods were receiving the feather-tipped prayers of the people and then were making their solemn farewell march to the ledge below the trail.

Night shut out the world of light, and in the kivas there was feasting and content. Bodies weary beyond thought of pain were tingling with the taste of food — green food, rich with flavor, abundant food for those who had starved. And for their hearts and mind, the crystal clarity of positive faith that rain or snow would tumble downward from the skies and feed their death-gripped fields as their long-deprived bodies had been fed by the moist tenderness of the sacred beans.

XIX. TRAILS AND A WATERLESS WORLD

WITH the first gray arc of dawn that bit into the black mass of night, some of the Hopi elders climbed the kiva ladders and looked eagerly toward the four quarters of the earth. Was the power of their ceremony working yet? Would the gods of the north send yellow-hued clouds filled with buoyant feathers of the snow? Would the Mongwi of the southern realm speed to them red, flame-shot clouds of warm, abundant rain?

With slow reluctance the sun stirred in his eastern sleep and wearily began his daytime labor of climbing to high zenith and then plodding to the limits of the west. The darkness brushed away, the world seemed no different from what it had for many dreary dawns.

The Bear Clan's chief of Hano narrowed his eyes with the hurt pain of one who fails to receive a confidently expected gift. Then, with an almost imperceptible shake of his gray, shaggy head, he turned to the others.

'It has been one day,' he said. 'Soon those clouds will come. Maybe tomorrow our Katchinas will send that rain we need.'

In Walpi, the thin, beady-eyed chief snapped at his wife when she asked him if rain would come. 'Rain *must* be on our fields within four days,' he growled. But even though he voiced his faith, yet all through the clear, cold day his patient family suffered under the prickling lash of words flung about by his nervous fear.

Pongkwiyo chirped and twittered like the bird she so resembled, but it was to hide her deep clutch of uneasiness. 'Nömsi, however, clinging to her sturdy faith in the little white cloud, which she knew was being nourished and cradled to return, was quiet and still as she went about her work; she even tried her hand at basket-making, although for some weeks she had not been able to find strength for more than the essential daily tasks. At least this old familiar occupation made her less poignantly aware of her thin, haggard son, 'Yeshva, who roamed aimlessly about, the newly gained strength of his manhood eaten away by the deep inroads of hunger.

Their faith in the power of the Pachava, a faith that spread through the length and breadth of the three towns, was so great that for most of the people hope resisted the defiant challenge of the rainless hours that had ended with the setting of the sun.

But a second day dawned — a day in no way different from the first. Morning swept in on an icy wind, dry and brittle as shale; noon for a time drew away the cold, until the passing of an orange sun tossed it back again.

That night the stars seemed to grimace from the sky. The moon seemed to stare like the face of the dead. Night shivered through to dawn — a third dawn — still without change.

Fear mounted like the rising numbness that fingers its way to frozen death. Defiantly the sun passed on, and then came soundless night with its mocking stars. The fourth dawn groped its way to day — and a still sun slithered in its changeless track and flung itself into dark.

In every town the anxious talk, the midnight meetings, the hope that had been bred by faith in ritual, yielded at last to silence — to utter nothingness. Eyes stared into the gray of walls — bodies sagged like storm-lashed clay...

Night passed.

In the morning, age seemed to have stripped Letaiyo of the last color-tone of youth. The ripple and flow of his manhood had subsided to the flat rut of existence without impulse. Time droned along, and his mind was as void of hope as the arching blue was destitute of clouds.

Had not the sins of the few been paid for by the dancing feet of the many? Had not months of ritual proved the faith of the Hopi people? The anger of the Feathered God, the serpent of the water world, must have been turned into cold, dead hate, unstirred by dance, by scattered meal, or the feathered tips of their many planted prayers.

In springtime the crow had worn green shoes and gods and men had raced in keen-edged competition. The first fruits of the harvest, so pitifully scant and few, had lain in the plaza as a mute reproach to the gods from eastern Hemisi who had danced in solemn splendor and then refused to send the rain. The snake brothers of the lower world had been brought from their deepest holes and held aloft for the gods to see, the gods who had veiled their eyes. And now, after months of sacrifice, of constant work and prayer, the Pachava gods of the universe, the mightiest beings of all that desert world, had been summoned by more than a hundred desperate men and had failed to send the rain.

The passing of that fourth cloudless day nearly killed the vital element of faith that had made Letaiyo's life a joyous one, a faith in the masked gods of the Katchina world. But still, the conviction that had come to him during the day and night in which he had brought his family from Mishongnovi still lingered in his mind, the conviction that faith, industry, and the possession of clean hearts and minds were the attributes of those who could win the favor of the gods.

If, then, after months of faithful performance, ceaseless industry, and rigorous self-denial, their ancient gods still refused to listen to their prayer, it must be that the people had not yet atoned for the sins that had brought about the suffering and destruction that was sweeping through the Hopi towns with the relentlessness of a wind-borne wall of lashing desert sand.

Then all at once a sudden thought found its way into the somberness of his mind, a thought that was as hopeful as the red flower of the cactus, a single spot of color in a dun-colored, dreary world: might it not be that the powers of another distant tribe, gods who had not been angered by the Hopi men, could be moved by the time-marked dancing that in all the ages of the past had brought the snow and rain? Perhaps in Sio, or Akuka, or far away with those Tewa to the east by the rivers of their legends, near the mountains of their gods, the pounded beat of the Hopi men might bring back health and rain.

Letaiyo turned to Polakka, who was sitting near-by

in the same semi-stupor of bewilderment that had borne down on all the men and turned their thin brown faces to still masks, as unchanging in expression as the faces of the gods whose favor could not be won.

'How many days' journey is it to those Tewa people that live so far away?' he asked.

Polakka looked at him in utter bewilderment. 'It is many, many days,' he answered. 'But why do you ask?' he inquired.

'Maybe those people have other gods who are not so mad with us. Maybe some of our Hopi people should go to those other towns. Maybe they have some meat there or little ears of corn. Maybe their springs have water. Maybe there we can live.'

'But the journey is too far! Our women and our little ones would die!' Polakka reasoned. 'For many days we should cross the sand, and then there would be mountains like our own Növatükyaovi. How could we do all this when we have so little food?'

'Here,' Letaiyo told him, 'there is nothing but death. Already many go away to Maski down below. Soon there will be so many that those who stay alive will give nothing to our dead ones — no food, no *potavi*. Then even their very souls are lost, they will wander far away and never reach that shadow land they seek.'

'It is true,' the Tewa man agreed. 'But should all our people go? Many are too old and cannot walk. For some there is still food. Let our men go to far places and our women stay at home.'

In Oraibi, far to the west, the same thought of departure had occurred to the village chief, and in the towns of the middle mesa the influence of Palalökong made them particularly anxious to flee.

Since the time of the dance across the dunes in Shongopavi that had angered him to frenzy, the madman had been dumb, but even though speech was taken from him he was as violent as ever. Whatever he could find he took, and even though the people hid their food and crept away when they saw him coming to their houses, still he seemed to be able to sniff his way to every concealed piece of dried meat or bowl of stewed corn. It was, in the opinion of everyone, further proof of his power. One mystery, though, had been cleared up by the daring act of a small boy.

He had seen Palalökong asleep — a snoring heap of foul odors — and the old man's mouth being open, the boy had suddenly peered inquisitively at him. Then, in high excitement, he had ventured nearer — looked closely and in shrill-voiced eagerness he had dashed about the town telling everyone that Palalökong had no tongue.

But with tongue or without it, he could still torture the men and women as even the twisting pangs of hunger could not do. So as the plans of many in all the Hopi towns began to be directed toward the exodus to the east, Mishongnovi led them all in numbers as the stealing hands and wordless screams of Palalökong made the thought of life in another land seem a delirium of joy.

Quietly, calmly, plans were made. Many of the people decided to go southeast to Zuni, as they knew that there they would find their friends, men who had come to Hopi in the days of rich prosperity and there been entertained. Others thought the high-rock town of Akuka would give to them the refuge that they sought. To some, the lower spread-out homes of Kawaika, near the Black Rock lands, seemed the haven they should seek; while to the Hano men, the fact that near the eastern river many kinsmen lived and flourished drew them toward that far-off stream that flowed and glistened in their minds. Large numbers of the women decided to accompany their men, among them 'Nömsi's oldest daughter, who decided to take her sister Flute Girl with her while the youngest of the sisters, Kwavöhuh, remained behind with their mother. With some of the people it was the fear of being left behind that determined such a course. With others, it was the fact that they had insufficient food on which to exist until the men should be able to return.

'Nömsi and Pongkwiyo, however, felt that they should stay. Each family had enough food remaining to keep its few members alive at least four moons — and by then surely their husbands would return.

For days upon days, from the lifting to the falling of the sun, black dots that were people moved across the brown menace of a waterless world. Some fixed their gaze on the southern sky as they plodded through the sand. Others headed into the higher east, down the rock-walled canyons, over the cedared hills. And south or east, many slowed in their foodless march and stayed, in sudden solitude, tiny heaps that cared no more for the sun that shone intensely or the distance of the trail.

A blue dress — a cotton cloak — a flash of storm-black wing or the excited swish of a furry tail — the steady cycle of life and death — ending, beginning, in a dual world of only sky and land.

Eastward, the sand-bedded canyon floors were dotted by the tracks of two men and two boys — tracks that showed quickened steps leading to the sheltered, shadowed lee where water might be found, and slow, uneven steps that staggered out to the sun again. Then out of the canyon land to a steady sea of flowing sand, sand that rose and fell in great smooth rounded waves, marked here and there with tiny little ripples as if it had been gouged by a giant scraping hand.

The long succession of tiny piles of kicked-back grains showed how deeply feet had sunk into its yielding mass. Beside the trail of one, a splotch of roughed space where its windblown, steady smoothness was marred by a sudden fall. Still, four pairs of feet had plowed ahead, though one dragged from track to track. Over the last dry vastness, toward heights with trace of green — toward trees and melting snowbanks, toward the river in the east.

Behind, a few women and old men were grimly facing time. Doling out each grain of corn — or water drop by drop. Hardening their resistance — clamping down on fear. Then the rising, falling, ever the same movement of the sun. Warm air succeeding winter, and heat beating warmth away. Old men tottering through the night, searching, prowling everywhere for a hidden pool of water or the seeping of a spring.

Quietly the women and girls lived on in the weather-torn house at the head of the Hano trail. The sure friendliness that had always bonded the two families was toughened by their need. To Pongkwiyo, the still strength of 'Nömsi was greater sustenance than the fragmentary dole of corn or the shreds of long-dried meat; while to the woman from Mishongnovi the cheer and readiness to smile of her tiny Hano friend was the drop that kept adhesive the dried-out elements of her courage. As long as they could be together, they could win the fight with time.

The girls, too, found in each other the substance that would nourish their own small grains of courage. Eagle-Breast-Feather was but a few years older than Butterfly Girl, and in her was much of the sturdiness, the quiet certainty, that marked the deeds of her Mishongnovi mother. Now the swift vigor of her blood that had given copper tints to her smooth young cheeks had slowed, and the cheeks had sagged with looseness like old age. Butterfly Girl, too, was only bone — with withered folds of dull gray-brown covering all but her eyes.

Still, even with the mutual help that gave them the strength of unity, each day became just a minute nibble of food and a sip of water drawn down by thick dry throats, and then the heavy-footed plodding of black, barren hours to another deadened day.

Three times the moon swelled and waned. And the amount of food that had been planned for one day's needs then had to last for two.

It was during the hottest days of the fourth full moon that Pongkwiyo came in at the door of her house with her hands twisting and her eyes like blackest beetles as she shook with muted anger. 'Nömsi looked at her in gray-eyed bewilderment.

'It is those bad ones — over there.' The Tewa woman motioned, waving to the right of her door. 'Do we not have enough hard time? But no, they must make big trouble — they ——' She flung her hands upward in an attitude of utter despair.

Then she reached out to her companion. 'You are our friend. You give us strength. You give us faith and hope. And those bad ones say it is wrong for Hopi woman to live with Tewa. They say that Tewa starve, and why should Hopi eat our food? I tell them those Hopi friends came to us with food from their own home; that still they eat that food and do not take from us. Then those women yell at me and howl that Hopi do not bring with them that water that they get. They make me mad, those Tewa, and I say these Hopi are my friends, that if I have some food and maybe some water too, what I have belongs to those who live with me and call me friend. Then that bad one in that house' — she motioned again to the right — 'wants to know why don't I give to her my bit of food. She say her mother now is dead — her boy has gone and now she will go soon; that if I have some food it belongs to Tewa people, and they will take it and let me die if our Hopi friend stay with us in our home.'

'Maybe they are right,' said 'Nömsi. 'Maybe we should go back to Mishongnovi.'

'No!' screamed the excited little Pongkwiyo. 'I say that if our friend goes, maybe we will be dead when our men come from those eastern lands. 'Nömsi must not go home. She must stay here with her Tewa friends.'

Sikyanömsi smiled grimly and touched her friend's head with her hand, as if in reassurance. It had not been easy for her to endure, first the chill of hostile eyes, then the gradual increase of actual menace as starvation burned to ash all the kindly impulses, the easy friendliness that had made the Hano people famed for their hospitality. It had been a bitter experience to see kindness die and hate flicker in its place. Still, she had seen these women's children lie gasping on the hot, dry ground; she had seen their elders fall in final surrender to the drought; while the strength of mid-maturity that kept life locked within itself made their suffering the greater as their fighting vigor retreated day by day.

In a very few, instead of ash, the constant burn of hunger had left a precious substance that could not be melted down. With the old town chief the thoughtfulness that had made him so much loved had sent his thin-boned body searching through the night, and not one night but many nights, to look for hidden springs. Then one day in the flaming sun of a morning he had climbed the Hano trail with an earthen jug of water, and to every house in town he had given a little trickle of brackish liquid strength. Some had screamed for more and cursed him when he gave the same to each; others had looked their thankfulness and breathed deep with new life.

Four moons had come, and when they left the men had told them all that by the fourth moon they would come again bringing corn and meat. But before another moon lifted its newborn form no trace of food could possibly remain. And then? 'Nömsi flung the thought from her mind and faced the reality of the present. Should she stay in Hano? Should she make her friend endure the anger of the other women? She knew well that her presence steadied Pongkwiyo and made her braver; yet, if those women should carry out their threat and rob the Tewa family of their tiny bit of food as penalty for harboring a Hopi from another town — her dry, blistered lips thinned in a hard line as her mind fought over the problem she must solve. And if she did leave — that would mean Mishongnovi and Palalökong; it would mean a night of crawling through the dark.

Two more days passed and the fourth moon began to wane. Then, late in the afternoon, a vengeful clawing wedge of women pushed in through Pongkwiyo's door and were confronted by the bitter-eyed Sikyanömsi, who pushed her Tewa friend behind her as she determined to fight her battles alone.

Out of the clamor one new thought forced its way to clarity. There had been shrieks of 'we warned you!' — 'She must go!' — 'Drive her out!' — 'Kill her if she stays!' And then all at once reason came like a sudden sun-flash as one woman shrilled her thought: 'She had that Palalökong stay at her house; maybe some of that man's meanness is in her now and that is why our children die.'

'So' — 'Nömsi spat at them — 'you want me to go because that Palalökong was in my house — because he ate my food and made my boy and girl go hungry!' For a moment she hesitated and looked around her, then she flung herself down on the floor. 'That man's curse is everywhere! I leave my home because of him. My men go far and maybe die because that man won't let it rain — and now it is because of that *powaka* that I have to leave my friend.' People she could fight, women she could defy, but the Feathered Serpent of the water world was a power to whom only surrender was possible.

So still sitting on the floor she faced the crowd. The fighting determination in her face was drained away, and there was only weariness and the bleakness of defeat.

'We go home,' she said. 'We go home tonight.'

Pongkwiyo in dismay looked at her as if all hope of life had been torn out of her little body. Sikyanömsi turned with a lifeless smile. 'You have one small girl who needs you. Soon our men will come home maybe, and we can be happy once more.'

Then, with a return of the former flash and with a streak of fire running through her words, she stood up and pushed the crowd of women back with the power of her wrath:

'But you! — I say to you that in all that we do in Hopi one thing is sacred above all. Our fathers tell us that each one who comes to our door, even if he is Navajo or someone else we hate, we must feed him and give him drink. Since those first days of our tribe it has been that way. I say to you that if your fathers could see what you do now, they would go away ashamed.'

Defiantly she slammed the door on the last of the crowd, and in an agony of exhaustion she buried her head in the lap of her friend. Minutes passed, a small stretch of time untouched by sound. Then, lifting her head once more, Sikyanömsi smiled at the tiny Tewa face of which she was so fond.

'You are not to be sad. Soon all will be well, and happiness will come rushing through our door. Then — who can tell? — perhaps new life will come from this friendship that is ours. My boy — your girl — maybe, who can tell?'

XX. THE MERGING OF LIFE AND DEATH

In Hano and the villages of the east there was still no food, and death moved in with increasing swiftness. In Walpi the streets were lined with the drying, rotting bodies of those who less than a year ago had flung color through the Pachava-celebrating town. Those who lived had lost all aspect of humanity. It was even whispered and believed that one young girl who had disappeared had been made to die to feed the bodies of those who clutched so frantically at life. Some few shivered at the thought that men they knew could kill their kin and let their bodies and their blood glut their maddened appetites.

The ugly heads and broad black wings of buzzards flapped in the dead-strewn streets and the sound slithered into the hearts of men, of human flesh torn and clawed by these birds of prey.

Pongkwiyo, the only one in all of those three towns to have a minute bit of food, hid what she had and divided it with her daughter in the stillness of the night. She tried to make the rest believe that she too was destitute of corn and meat, but she knew that she had failed to convince them — she caught in their planning, speculating eyes the knowledge of her lie.

The sun was vanishing to make way for the rising of a small sixth moon when she and her child left the house one day for a final search, to see if, somewhere along that dreary line of earth and sky, by some remotest chance their men might yet be seen.

But there was only a moving wall of dust that had reared itself in anger and wrestled with the wind.

Butterfly Girl probed the sand-broken waves of shimmering heat with steady, staring eyes, until all at once she put her hands before her face and stumbled with sudden dizziness. Clutching for support, she fell against the splinter-rough bar at the side of a sheep corral. Her bare arm scratched along the pole and its jagged wooden barbs cut deep into her young flesh. Blinking her eyes in an effort to collect her senses, she looked at the blood that had been drawn — blood — she looked at it in confused, dull bewilderment.

A slight sound caused her to raise her eyes. Then all at once terror ripped like lightning through her being. Her scream ended in a moan as she sank cowering, defenseless, to the ground, for before her she had seen a long, thin face — a face with eyes that shone and stared at the trickling blood — lips that moved like the jaws of a beast snarling after food.

Pongkwiyo, too, had seen, and with the swiftness of a defending bird that thinks of nothing but how to save its young, she hurled her tiny body before that of her child.

'Back! Go back!' she screamed to the girl. 'Bar the door and stay there in that dark!' Then, with black beads of eyes that snapped with flame, she met stare with stare. Step by step she forced back the half-crazed man, who slowly lost the beastliness that glinted from his eyes and at last slouched away. Pongkwiyo's breath came jerking back like the banging beat of her heart. Cautiously she looked about: the door of her house was tightly closed and not a soul could now be seen — except one poor bird-riddled form that lay beside the road.

Like the drawing pinch of a deep, old wound the Tewa woman could still feel the memory of those eyes staring at the blood on her child's arm, the scar of that sudden stab of fear. In doubtful hesitation she lingered, then crossed to her door, rapped and whispered for some time until it opened fearfully to let her dart inside.

All through the night the mother cradled and tightly held her child. Then, when dawn pushed gently in, she led her to the blackened space for storage, where masks were kept, and to which there was no entrance except through that one front room.

'You must stay there and make no sound,' Pongkwiyo cautioned her still frightened child. 'Your mother will be in this room outside and never go away.'

Two days passed, and then a third; then came a bang upon the door. The mother lay there tense and still — heard whispers from the dark.

'She, too, is dead,' came from the night. 'Dead like all the rest.'

Then silence — darkness — sun again, and a day of vanished food.

Two foodless days, and then likewise the last drop from the jug. And time meant nothing — light and dark — what matter which was which?

Mishongnovi was a dreary waste — a heat-riddled heap of mute, deserted homes. Here and there life fluttered in final effort before the stillness of release. Wolves, thin as the starving Hopi men, lurked about the village streets — wolves that meant life or death; food for the famine-stricken people if trapping snared them; otherwise — a crunch of bones that once were active men.

'Nömsi looked at her empty hands and at the still form of her child. For two days there had been no food — just a drop or two of water — and the fifth moon swelled in the sky.

Where were her men? Had they ever reached that Tewa land beyond the eastern river? Where were they now? Perhaps — somewhere — among those mountain rocks — or in some distant stretch of desert sand — only the gods could tell.

Thoughts from the past dragged pictures into her brain. Thoughts of the man who had claimed her youth — thoughts of the son who had been reborn. And now? For them perhaps just sun and sand, and for her — in a day or two — the end of a long life trail.

The still form on the floor moved. Then the bones of a hand moved without purpose vaguely toward the bones of a dry, hot face — a face that was young in the seasons it had known, but that had crowded the withering force of years into the space of as many weeks.

'Is there yet no food?' The voice was thick with thirst.

'Nömsi looked at her daughter with lead in her eyes and her heart. '*Ka'eh* — no — we have no food,' she said. 'But maybe' — she hesitated — 'maybe tonight your grandfather will catch that wolf that makes that awful howl. Or maybe — like that other day — we shall find some little mouse.'

A confused pounding on the barred door brought her to hushed but alert stillness. From without, the throaty, guttural wails of Palalökong came to them.

'Nömsi was rigid with fear. Her eyes glinted defensively from the blackness of their sockets; the hanging folds of skin that had been her food-providing breasts were still with breathlessness. Her hands were poised, inanimate in the air as she looked fearfully at her child. For some time the moans continued; then they died away.

'Never must we let him in!' The mother trembled out the words. 'Better that we die inside than have that man come here.'

An hour passed. Then again a sound was heard at the door. This time, however, instead of a mad banging, there was system in the four clear knocks. With as much effort as if she had been pulling herself out of a mire, Sikyanömsi drew herself to her feet.

'It is Makya,' she whispered.

Then, slowly dragging her body, that reluctantly obeyed a tired brain, she fumbled at the door until a rush of hot dry air billowed into the room and with it a shrunken figure of unearthly whiteness: hair like a spider's web; hands like an eagle's claws, but a face dominated by a still power that seemed to have risen above all human need.

The ancient hunter, who had outlived all those who knew his youth, barred the door and then reached inside the folds of his dusty, dark blue shirt.

'Take this,' he directed as he handed them some bone. With wonder the woman and her child looked at it; then, as dry gristle touched their mouths, they began to whimper with the release of hunger, so very long denied. Much time passed while they gnawed and gnawed, trying to crush the solid bone, while Makya watched them eat — watched while solemn grimness crept over his face. All at once, Sikyanömsi looked up from the bone and saw the face of Makya — but on it an expression such as she had never seen in all the years of her life.

'Mayka!' she demanded. 'Why do you look that way?'

The old man kept silent, but his eyes were as if he had just looked on the world of straining, tortured souls beating their way through the cactus path to the shadow world.

'Makya!' The voice that was flung at him was frantic, like an animal trapped by death. 'Makya! What *is* it?'

Against his will the old warrior's gaze moved with a twitch and a shudder to the bone in his daughter's hand. Still afraid and still completely uncomprehending, Sikyanömsi looked down at the bone — then up again at the old man.

'Makya,' she whispered as enlightenment came. 'Is *this* — did *you* go to that place where we bury our ——?' With a gesture of loathing she flung the bone from her, and her head fell to her knees as she quivered with tearless sobbing.

Makya looked at her with the tender comprehension of old age.

'My child,' he reasoned softly, 'I know how you must feel. Still, those people — that we buried there — those ancient ones — whose bones have dried — they are those people who long ago once gave us life. Here they lived — and danced — and sang. Here they died — and went to their peace — in that shadow world. Is it not true — that they would gladly give — this life to us again? They know we must not die. That we must find — some strength — to wait for those men — who will come to us — with water and with corn.'

Another day passed, and in the dimness of dusk Sikyanömsi pulled her way out-of-doors, while her child barred the door behind her in case Palalökong should return.

Out in the desert world there was the eternal sameness of a red sun dropping in a purple west. The same yellowing blue stretched from all the quarters of the earth. Toward the south, spiraled dust twirled its curving way. For a moment memory stirred in the woman as the spout of sand made her think of the mocking words of the Tewa. That whirlwind was the sister-in-law of Mishongnovi they had jeered. For had not a man, long in the past, married a beautiful girl who had swept him away in the wind she was? Bah! Those Tewa women who had driven her away. Those women who could be so cruel. Still — were they really wrong? Could anyone fight against the power of the god who owns the sea that underlies the earth?

As if in answer to her thought, Palalökong crept into sight. No one had food for him any more, yet he kept himself alive with ants and beetles and filth. From time to time his fury still lashed out at the people — at the people who died — some every day — in the houses with no one left to bury them; in the streets where they were dragged off by the wolves.

'Nömsi tried desperately not to see the hideous proofs of these horrors that were scattered about, even in front of her door. Rags of blue dresses smeared with red — torn bits of blanket-wool — a chewed shred of moccasin. She shuffled past with eyes that watched the path, but tried in vain to screen from consciousness all that lay beside it.

To stay within the house meant watching in utter helplessness while the last life left to her, of all those she had borne, was slowly murdered by the famine's tightening hold. Inside there was the unyielding force of the drought's destructiveness. Out in the sun, the horror that came afterward.

In all this vastness of heat-swept, unbarred space, no sign of life at all — except the mark of paws in the dust, or the drooping yellow cactus shapes that bristled their defiance of the sun, and even now, in certain lights, seemed to be faintly green.

Who would be next? the woman thought. But then, why think when thought makes tragedy more real — when thought crushes like a falling boulder on the brain — on the brain that otherwise is strangely light and empty, like the body which is air as long as it is still, and then, when movement has to be, is turned to solid stone?

Where were her men? When — when — where?

Sound caught at the gray dullness of her mind. Scraping sound, that, as she turned to look, became the noise of an old, worn woman, clinging to the ground, but moving bit by bit toward the drooping, yellow-green oval shapes whose wrinkled leaves, to her misted eyes, were food of softness, rich with taste.

Horror knit with tension the wandering vagueness of Sikyanömsi's brain. But speech withered in her throat.

Slowly, with persistence, the old woman dragged along, clawed at the plant with senseless hands and never felt the spines, chewed in her drought-dried mouth — and then, whipped with pain, beat at her swelling throat and writhed, while life was stifled in her breast.

'Nömsi beat her bony hands despairingly at her brain as she staggered back to her house and her child.

That woman once had been her friend — one of those who had walked with her and the newborn child Kwa-yeshva, walked to the ledge, to the rising sun, and there had named him with the rest.

How could life pass so horribly?

Where were the gods who had made them sing and shout with joy in those distant days when rain had come to the desert earth? Shadow and tortured memory shut out light and hope; shoved reason into blankness and made of life a dull, dim flicker on the borderland of death.

When day returned, 'Nömsi's eyes were glazed as she lay beside her child — the 'feather from an eagle's breast' that no longer was a buoyant prayer wafted to the gods, but the hanging white inertness laid on a dead man's hair.

Makya too lay near the girl, and his ancient eyes watched closely for the end of her short life trail — for in him one thought gave will to live: when the time came for these two, somehow he would give them burial, would let them face the east, would place on them the *potavi*, the cotton path, the slender strand, that would lead them to their fathers. Then for him there would have to be the silence of extinction — no burial — no spirit land — just death.

A vigorous rap on the door — a sound far more backed by energy than any he had heard — brought him to his feet. At first the old man hesitated; then the knocking continued and gained in vigor. There was no wild banging, as there was when Palalökong tried to enter; just a decisive rapping, so finally Makya unlatched the door and peered through the crack, like an animal warily emerging from its lair.

'*Aie*,' he ejaculated with dumbfounded awe. 'Castile,' he whispered in complete disbelief. 'Castile.'

XXI. THE BARTER OF YOUTH FOR CORN

STANDING outside was a sturdy, swarthy, whiskered man. For a second Makya looked at him with dumbfounded awe. 'Castile,' he whispered again. 'Castile.'

'*Usted hablar español?*' the Mexican inquired with a business-like air. Memories plucked from fifty years before, when he had labored for a short time in a white man's town, slowly filtered into Makya's brain.

'*Español*' — he spoke the word with the wonderment of a little child. '*Si — poco. Nö Castil'tuhkaita,*' he added, reverting to the speech of his fathers. Then, '*A-ah!*' he gasped as he looked past the man and saw on the ledge below a covered wagon, two mules, and in the shadow under the rounded canvas, corn and barreled water.

In crazed eagerness, the old man started for it, but the Mexican held him back.

'Not yet,' he said firmly. 'We need some young girls to work for us. We will buy these girls with food. You got any girls?' he asked.

It took some time for old Makya even partially to understand. Anyhow, one thought defied all others for consideration: his child and her child were dying for need of water and food. Here was that water, here was that food, and there might still be time to bring them back to the conscious land of the earth's surface.

'Yes,' he declared eagerly. 'We have girl. Good girl, but you must first give her some water or very soon she will die.'

'*Bueno*,' the Mexican agreed, not understanding all the old warrior's words, but sensing his meaning. While the strangely active visitor hurried down to the wagon, Makya stared after him; then, as his dim eyes realized that a barrel was being tipped and his keen ears heard the gurgling sound of water splashing in a bowl, little whimpering cries jerked out from his lips and his thin, white mouth twitched without control.

It was but a meager drop of water that the Mexican handed to the old man; he was too shrewd a bargainer to give more, and he looked critically at the women, while Makya, with the tenderness of a mother, lifted the heads of first Sikyanömsi and then young Eagle-Breast-Feather, who half opened their eyes as the water touched their dry, coated throats.

'I don't think she's worth much,' the trader declared, with disparaging appraisal, as he looked at the girl, who was slowly brushing her way through the mists back to life. 'Still,' he concluded, 'she seems to be young all right, and I guess she's used to hard work. How about some others?' He turned to Makya with the question: 'Are there many other young girls in this town?'

For a moment the ancient Hopi stared at the other perplexedly. Then gradually it dawned on the old man what the Mexican's words had really meant: that their little girl — the only one remaining — would have to go away, quite far away, with this strange Castile man, away from her family to an unknown land.

Abruptly the man interrupted Makya's thought by making a trip to the wagon and returning with a sack of corn, which he dumped unceremoniously on the floor.

'Give me a jug and I'll give you more water,' he announced. 'That is, if you are ready to shake hands on its being a trade,' he concluded, and he eyed the aged grandfather while his lips pursed and his eyes narrowed in crafty watching.

All through this procedure Sikyanömsi had been fighting with the elusive workings of her mind. Water — corn — an unknown man — what was it all?

As slowly as if death hung at his heels, Makya reached for the jug that for so long had hung dry on the wall. Then, holding it limply by his side, he paused while thought strove to become decision in the weary numbness of his mind.

After a moment he put his free right hand, his thin, weak hand, on the vigorous stranger's arm. 'Why do you want our girl?' he asked. 'Why do you not just give us some little corn and maybe some water too and then go back to your home? Why should our child go away?'

The Mexican started to answer impatiently. Then with a shrug he changed his mood and grinned good-humoredly. He could understand hardly a word that old Makya said. Still, you couldn't really blame these people for asking questions.

'We will give her a good home,' he promised. 'We have to have more girls to work in our houses and maybe a boy or two to be in our fields. So when we heard that you Hopi people had no food, we thought it would be a fair trade. She'll be happy. And perhaps some day, when she is older, she can come back again. But how about some other girls? Maybe in the other houses there are more?' he questioned eagerly.

Makya shook his head. 'Maybe some few — most of us are old and many die — others went away.' The old patriarch's face was gray as the ageless rock; in ceremony he had never worn a more complete mask. Water — corn — slavery for their child in return for life. Then he looked at 'Nömsi, and as he saw the haggard face that had been lashed to numbness by hunger and thirst, he knew that he could not let her die; knew that the Breast-Feather of an Eagle, the symbol of prayer and hope, must vanish to a land of strange gods and cruel men. His head was bowed in hopeless acquiescence as he reached out and touched the Mexican's hand to conclude the trade.

'Fine,' responded the other, smiling broadly. 'Now we must go to other houses and to other towns. Early to-morrow we shall come back. You have girl all ready. 'Then, as he saw the old man failed to understand: '*Mañana* — early — when sun comes up.' He illustrated his words with an upward motion of his palm.

'*Si*,' Makya nodded. '*Kavo*.' He lifted his stark face, and for a moment his dim eyes tried to probe the bearded countenance before him, as if he might be able to read in it a vision of the future for the child they were to lose.

'You give that girl some food now,' the Mexican directed, turning his eyes to the door. 'I tell you what I do,' he added, with a sudden impulse, although his eyes still failed to meet those of the old chief, 'I will get some bread from my wagon. You give her that and then some water with it.'

Once more he hurried down the trail, and returned with a half loaf which he handed to Makya. 'Well, *adios, amigo*' — he waved his hand. '*Hasta mañana*.'

Sikyanömsi's eyes were now open wide, but the gaze that she concentrated on the bread was that of one who looks knowingly at one of the mirages that frequently silver the desert scene. Her expression never changed as she watched Makya break off a piece, dip it in some water, and then offer it to her. She stared at the bread, but her stiff, dry lips never moved. Gently her father poked them apart with his fingers and then placed the wet food in her mouth. A slow wave of incredulity swept across her eyes as her thick tongue moved and her choked throat managed to draw down this messenger of life regained.

Eagle-Breast-Feather, all unaware that her life was the price for this food, opened her mouth with the unquestioning receptivity of an infant bird. Finally, with a sigh of tension released, Makya, too, took a mouthful of food and gulped it down, then more and more as his suddenly awakened senses realized their need.

Slowly, with infinite patience, Makya fed the others bit by bit until finally Sikyanömsi motioned to the old man to help her to sit up. As she did so, she looked about and seemed at last to grasp the reality of food — food and water that darkened the outside of the old pot hanging on the wall.

'Who — was — that — man?' The words could hardly be heard. 'Where — did — he — get — corn?' Her bewilderment increased as she read the anguished look in the old man's eyes.

With the soothing gentleness of a mother who brushes

aside the questioning of a sick child, Makya quieted her with crumbs of moist bread and gradually caressed her across the borderland of sleep. Then in stoic grimness the ancient warrior sat and pondered how he should tell the horror of the barter that must follow the rising of the sun.

When white light first pushed its way into the dust-filled room, 'Nömsi stirred and was again given food and water by her father. Then the girl woke, and a half smile of delight pushed up the cracked stiffness of her cheeks as she felt an inner surge of strength and realized that at last dawn was not to be a time of waking to hopeless pain.

When 'Nömsi again questioned him, Makya looked at her compassionately while he gathered together his words.

'In all our Hopi ways,' he said at last, 'one rule we always keep. For what we get — we give return. That is our Hopi rule. When we dance and ask our gods for rain, we give them food and prayer, and always we must work to show our hearts are right and that we earn that which we all need. When our men decide to work, and help to build some house, that woman whose new house they build must make for them much food. So now that this strange man, this Castile, gave us life, we must give it in return. That is our Hopi rule — that is our Hopi way.'

'But what life can we give?' Sikyanömsi asked in bewilderment.

In answer Makya pointed to the girl. 'There is that life,' he said.

In response to uncontrollable instinct, 'Nömsi placed her arm across the girl, who looked wide-eyed at the thin, white form of her very ancient grandfather.

A minute or two passed while the mother still groped desperately for the real meaning of his words.

'Why should they want *her* life?' she asked. 'What is she to those strange ones who come from some other world?'

'Who knows how those Castile think?' The old man gave a helpless shrug. 'They say that they have work to do — in their houses and in their fields. They come to all our villages and take our starving girls. If we say "No," then all must die — how can we choose? How can we know what it is right for us to do?'

Wide-eyed with horror, Sikyanömsi stared at him as he continued, 'Is it better that she should live in some strange place with those who do not know her gods?'

'No, no!' 'Nömsi shrilled while her arm clutched her daughter close. 'It is better that we die at home. My man is gone — my boy — who knows? My other girl and her sister with her man may all be dead. This one must stay and die with us — not in some place that is far away.'

Eagle-Breast-Feather looked at her mother. For weeks her life had brushed that of the shadow world. Torture had burned fear away; horror had bred in her the quiet wisdom of the aged. Still it was youth that spoke, spoke in the innocent that knows the dawn's clear light. And while speech still came thickly from her lips it rushed like a mountain stream from her heart.

'I am not some little girl. I am now quite big,' she said. 'I think I know what it is right that I should do.'

She smiled and touched a thin braid of her mother's hair. 'Why should you die?' she asked. 'I want you to live some more when our men come home and my sisters too. Then some day rain will come and I will look at those clouds and think of our Hopi fields and those corn ears that will wave in summer air. I am not afraid,' she reassured her mother. 'Those men may be good to me. I can work, and if I do, then may be — they will treat me well.'

She smiled again at her mother in all the confident innocence of her youth.

'Perhaps, some time when years go by, maybe I can come back to our own Mishongnovi, and then I shall see lots of little ones, and maybe in Hano 'Yeshva will be living, and maybe there will be many little ones there as well.'

As the white light yielded to the yellow glow and the crimson flush of a dawning sun spread across the east, the mother love of 'Nömsi battled with the youth and reason of her child. The uncertainty of what lay ahead; the thought that maybe her girl would have to bear strange babies with pale yellow faces, that perhaps those Mexicans would be cruel and beat her — all these things clutched at the wearied essence of her brain, the brain that had been made to work so madly after it had been dragged back from the peace and easy slowness of the shadowland near death.

At the same time 'Nömsi was tempted almost beyond resistance by the thought that if now she were to live perhaps she might see 'Yeshva and even cherish the tiny beings who would be mothered by Pongkwiyo's little girl.

Other homes were being torn — in high Shipaulovi and the western town of the middle mesa. In each, the question was ripping reason and tenderness into shreds of normal emotion. Should their children stay to die or go into the unknown?

When the rising heat of early morning pushed its way westward from the dawn, again the wagon stood by the towering rock that gave Mishongnovi its name, and there young girls and a few small boys were placed beneath the rounded canvas. Then came the groan of wagon wheels creaking down a sandy road; the lurching arch of protecting white staggering to the south and finally out across the gray-brown waste, a spot still white that slowly turned to dark, and then was a tiny streak that vanished behind the farthest hill.

In all the three towns people watched — people who had known the miracle of water trickling down the throats that had rattled with the groping touch of death; people who now lived to know the torture of uncertainty and fear for those whose lives they had guarded and watched and slowly seen unfold.

They had bought their own lives and the lives of their other young ones through the sale of these girls and boys — yet what else could they have done? Was not life, even a life of fear, to be preferred to death? But each one knew that in all the years to come they would pay and pay with memory, and that the solid rock which towered there before them would always stand and stare at them as if with eyes that had seen and known the day when they had sold their young to slavery and sent them out to the blankness of the unknown.

XXII. THE SPEAR OF THE GOD OF ZENITH

In the rock-walled house by the southern tip of Mishongnovi life slowly flowed back into sluggish veins; strength stirred itself out of the lethargy of weakness, but it was life and strength that were mockery. Every sip of the precious water, every ground particle of corn, was an inevitable reminder of the child, the young Eagle-Breast-Feather, whose life was the purchase price for that water and that corn.

To Makya, the life that stole back into his ancient being meant clearer thought regained. So for hour after hour he sat and pondered the meaning of all the desolation that surrounded them, and the reason for the graying of the embers that had once been sparkling life.

Why had that Palalökong brought it all? Perhaps, he thought, it might have been because through all that Feathered Serpent's years of oldest age he always had had to suffer from the jeering, sneering meanness of uncomprehending youth. They had slung him in the dirt and dung and mocked him when he fell. It was no wonder they were punished for the wrong that they had done.

But now perhaps the sin had been atoned for; maybe now two years of slow starvation and the final tragedy of slavery for their young ones were sufficient expiation for the harm that had been done. Now it might be that at last the gods would listen to man's prayer and heed the dancing feet of those who called for rain. Makya pondered this at great length; then one night he called together all the old men of the town. Quietly and earnestly he told them what he thought.

In the long-deserted kiva they sat about — twenty old men who were like as many gaunt specters from the shadow world. To some of them the months, the years of unanswered ceremony had crushed the faith that had been a buoyant force all through their younger manhood. Day after day, night after night, all through these two tragic years they had attended faithfully to the myriad details of their exacting rites. But each one had been followed by barren sky and the utter mockery of steel-blue space cut each day by an unrelenting sun.

In dull apathy they listened to Makya's plea. Weakness, weariness, and hopelessness made them almost devoid of feeling except that of resignation to the inevitable end. Still, it was true that out of an utterly unknown world food and drink had been brought to them — even though to some of them it had brought hatred for the life that had been regained. Makya seized upon this point in his effort to arouse in them some interest, some response. Could it not be, he argued, that this was the turning-point, that now perhaps the road once more led to the renewed favor of the gods?

Finally a tiny spark of interest flashed in some of them, and this Makya fanned to definite plan. They must dance, he pleaded, dance once more for the rain, dance for the aid of the gods of zenith and the four quarters of the world.

Slowly out of the mire of apathy, the thought of certain songs grew into the desire to hear them once again. Then argument about the songs sharpened these thoughts into defense and attack. The bickering about what they might sing and how they might dance brought to many of the men the feeling that something from the old days had been recaptured; that it was really not so hopeless after all.

Makya then capped it all by declaring with all the vehemence of which his ancient voice was capable that no one must take part who could not do so with faith in the successful outcome of the dance. To this, with surprising readiness, most of them agreed, so before the meeting was over they were all thoroughly excited about the plan. To some the only doubt that held them back was a grave doubt of their physical ability to endure the strain now that their bodies were so weak and thin.

Still, it was agreed that the following night they would begin their practice, and that in eight days they would once more court the aid of the gods with rhythm for the rain, once more their rattles would sound and their tired old voices would shout in prayer across the dreary waste of a drought-killed land.

The women and the few remaining children were delighted with the plan, not only because it gave them hope, but because it would be such a notable event after the hideous monotony of so many tragic months.

For three nights the kiva echoed with the quavering voices and feeble stamp of their rehearsal. Now that they had actually begun, they were all thrilled by what they did.

The women likewise planned just what they should do to win back the favor of the gods. Food there must be, so each one made some meal from the precious bartered ears of corn and in tense excitement prepared to bake when the day drew near. Still, for many of the aged men and the worn-out ghosts of women, dizziness, weakness, or the grip of pain came back to mock at them for thinking that they could forget the bodies that even now were fed with but tiny pinches of guarded food.

Sikyanömsi had moved about for many days, for slowly unrolled weeks, in a haze that was jabbed by poignant thought. Those swarthy men — her child — what would be her life? The complete uncertainty of the fate of Letaiyo, 'Yeshva, Kwamana and Flute Girl had not crushed her the way this last tragedy had done. For the journey of the men had been a quiet departure and one that was inevitable and planned. On the other hand, the whiskered face of the Mexican leered at her in memory, and the eternal mass of the great Corn Rock that had seen the final bartering reared its solid hugeness in front of her very house.

These new plans, though, had brought a sudden demand on her tenderness and care. Makya was so old — there was no one else as old as he — and now he limped about and bolstered up the courage of the rest. She must watch him, guard him, give him food; and thus the love and devotion that she had always felt for the old man lifted her finally out of the soddenness of her misery and thought.

Early in the morning after the fourth rehearsal, 'Nömsi went outdoors. The sun was rising, but the heat was not so great, for summer was passing on to fall. For a few minutes she stood facing the east; then, picking up a bit of wood, she turned back toward her house. As she did so she looked up and, with a sudden cry of amazement and almost childlike joy, she dropped the stick and stumbled down into the kiva where Makya lay asleep.

'Makya! Makya!' she called. 'It has come — my cloud — that I knew would come again. Makya, come and see! It is that cloud that will bring us rain.'

Still dazed from his short sleep after the rehearsal in the night, Makya gripped her arm and pulled himself to his feet. Up the kiva ladder they went, and from the roof they stared at the tiny ball of white that clung to the sacred mountain in the west.

'It is that little one — I *know* it is my cloud,' 'Nömsi insisted. 'When that Hano woman died, she sent herself away to feed that cloud and give it strength to come back to us again. Makya, she urged, 'now your men must dance! They must sing! Your priests must blow smoke to that cloud — we must help it to grow big. Makya, tell your men that if they dance, now our rain will come.'

Her enthusiasm was so sure, so fervent her belief, that Makya scurried about dragging out reluctant, disbelieving men, who kept insisting that they must not dance until the day for which they had planned. But while they argued, the small white cloud began to grow, and then 'Nömsi clutched at them vowing that storm was near and beseeching them to aid the cloud to grow and bear the rain.

So thin, gaunt men fumbled and searched for costume parts while other women came to help 'Nömsi, who by that time was quite prepared to dress them and even to dance or sing herself if the others failed to respond to her plea.

The whiteness of the cloud became smeared with dark streaks, and out across the western height it spread until it filled that entire part of the sky. Up through the kiva entrance came the men like the ancients long ago, who had climbed a spruce to freedom and the surface land of earth. Then the rattle of a dried-out drum, the shiver of a gourd, and the tramp of aged feet was sounded on the long-neglected ground. The reedy voices of the old piped their longed-for prayer, and if their footsteps stumbled and their knees shook as they danced, as the clouds loomed up their faith grew strong and their arms reached toward the sky.

'Nömsi stood on the edge of the village square, and in her exaltation and frenzied eagerness her hands were tearing at her dress and her breath came in gasps and moans. Then, all at once, her arms fell in mute despair as she saw the bowed figure of Palalökong totter onto the scene — Palalökong, who had lain inert for two days until people had dared to believe that he had died. The sound of ceremony had somehow penetrated to his brain and stirred in him hatred and defiance.

Makya and the rest also saw him come near and heard the wordless howl of his protest, but while they feared, with an inner cringing fear, still on they danced as the cloud rolled across the sky and spread out overhead. The screams of Palalökong grew more maddened as he sensed the moisture in the air and smelled the pungent fumes of smoke that were blown by priests from the kiva roof — smoke puffed toward the blackening clouds and the flash that cut the sky.

Then a few drops bounded in the dust while the women rushed home and reappeared with bowls, jars, and pots to catch each precious bit that came. With the frenzy of dawning freedom, they ran by Palalökong without show of fear, and the twisted, ranting madman screamed as he felt them pass.

The drops came then in a pounding stream, and still the old men danced while water beat on their age-worn heads and the wind tore at their hair. It caught at feathers and at cotton kilts; it tore in a maddened riot and it felt like a caress. For life danced in on those drops of rain, and each flame that seared the clouds was the spear of the god of zenith as he charged upon the drought.

Banks of sand broke away and slithered down below; rocks came loose and bounded off and still the rain came sweeping down. Water roared across the square and beat upon the breasts of women, who thrilled at the force that was thrust upon them as never in all their lives had they thrilled at the touch of the men by whom they had been wooed and won.

Battered, beaten, swamped with rain, Makya danced away, his feet in standing water and his heart a flame of joy.

High above the village boulders were poised, bedded in sand; sand that began to roll away with the rain until the sunken base of these mighty stones was freed and, as the driving water licked about it, one mammoth rock hung bare for a second; then it roared down on the little square; past the fleeing men it shot, until suddenly it caught up Palalökong, who was screaming in mad rage, and tossed him off into rain-filled space with a final smashing sound.

Miles away in Hano, Pongkwiyo lay in semi-consciousness. Butterfly Girl was in the dark, as she had been for days and days. The Tewa woman seemed to dream — she was being patted gently by a loving hand. The face of her man seemed to be before her, and so she smiled. The patting then turned to a steady knock and the knock to a mighty pound. The face, the dream, were swept away and she looked about in fear. The pound was a banging, maddened sound that made her cower in utter dread. Then all at once she realized that it came from without and above; it surrounded her, hemmed her in with its power and din. Fearfully her eyes moved about; in sheer disbelief she stared at the window as trickling lines on the window-pane arrested her incredulous eyes. Slowly but with dawning joy she recognized the howl of wind and the swishing splash of water pouring down. For an instant she trembled with shock; then, as her mind grew clearer, she realized what she must do — for that water outside could save them both if she could but get to the door.

Each movement cut like an arrow-point, but she dragged herself along until at last she unbarred the door and let it swing in the might of the rushing wind. The cold and wet bathed her with strength as she leaned against the lintel and yielded to the rain. Then her daughter's urgent need made her again shuffle across the floor, less feebly as her mind grasped the amazing reality of the storm. Then a little bowl was found, and outside by the step a pool of water that could be scooped into the bowl. Back to the dark where her daughter lay she went with the little pot that dripped on the dusty floor. The child's head was hot and dry, and even though Pongkwiyo trickled water into her mouth, it was some time before the girl was able to swallow.

Hours passed, and the wet shivering mother sat beside her child and gave her drop after drop of the moisture that had come so suddenly from the skies. Finally fevered eyes were opened and ears seemed to hear the constant repetition of Pongkwiyo: 'We have rain! We have rain!'

XXIII. LIFE COMES TO ANOTHER DAWN

THE storm marched across the sand from the coned mountains in the west to the long, walled canyons of the east. Its gray masses swept by the upthrust buttes, and its rain pelted and lashed at the desert that was so nearly dead with drought that for some time it lacked completely the power to absorb. So over the vast sage-rooted waste the water searched and ran until it pitched downward into the gouged-out washes that stretched like veins over the entire desert world. Then, as these deep, dry river beds still failed to grip the wet, in swirling turbulence it rose until high sand banks cracked and splashed as they dived into the stream.

From the east, over the cedar-crested hills, four men on burros loaded down with sacks of food slowly rode along, and with a sudden limp release from the grip with which they had fought the sun they yielded to the cool, sweet air; to the mounting freshness of the wind; to the arrows of the driving rain and the fighting force of the storm-borne blast. They had seen the rain walking with a mighty stride. They had seen the cloud gods pierce the earth in act of impregnation, killing the menace of the drought and thrusting life deep down into the soil.

Weeks and months passed while life slowly streamed

back to the mesa homes: human life from the east and south and desert life up through the moistened earth. With life regained there was work to do — work and ritual to satisfy the needs of gods and men.

In Mishongnovi two families gathered by a door to watch Soyala, god from the south, open the kivas for the winter rites. A gray sky shook itself and scattered snow — snow that would slowly yield its essence to the land — snow that would guard the earth for spring.

The green mask and embroidered robe of the Patki Clan's chief god were dotted with thick, fat melting flakes as he planted a feathered stick of prayer in the rolled-up reeds on the kiva roof — a prayer stick placed near the ladder which reached skyward through a rectangle of space — through the entrance that could not be barred — the *sipapuni* of man's emergence — the ancestral passage that led upward to new life, to the work of creating warmth and light and of building a new world.

'Nömsi and Pongkwiyo chattered away like the birds of spring. Life was such a buoyant flight of joy. They kept looking at their boy and girl and giggled as they talked.

'It won't be long before those peach trees bloom,' the former said. 'Then perhaps my boy goes to your home. Maybe he will wear that blanket Makya made and maybe you will all be mad and tear that blanket into bits.' She laughed at the absurdity of such an idea. 'But maybe, though, you will see that it is nice — thick and firm and soft with wool. So maybe you will let him stay and sleep in your house while it is so dark.'

Pongkwiyo beamed with joy. She knew that when Kwayeshva came to woo his girl at night his blanket would never be torn and he would be allowed to find her in the dark.

'It will be such fun,' she laughed. 'You and I will fight with mud and your sisters with my mother's girls. You will say that you are mad with us because we took your boy away. Then maybe I will chase you all around our house and put that soft wet mud right down your back and on your nice blue dress. You will look funny then,' she teased. 'You will be dirty and your sisters just as bad.'

'Maybe you think that we are weak and can't fight as well as you. I tell you I will take that mud and smear it on your face and hair.' Sikyanömsi jeered with glee. 'Then you will look much worse than I. You will be just as dirty as that Palalökong used to be.'

For a second she hesitated as if regretting her careless words. Then laughing joyously once more: 'Perhaps I shall take some little pot — some little pot of mud — and throw it so it breaks in two right on your muddy head.'

'Maybe if you do, then I shall get some bigger pot and make it fall on you,' Pongkwiyo taunted in return.

Then together they both sighed in the fullness of their joy.

For a time they sat there in reflective silence while the snow dropped lazily through the air.

'It will be nice when your girl comes to me with meal that she has ground. Then I shall take those "wheels" of hers and brush each hair and let it fall with 'Yeshva's in some bowl of suds. Then it will be black and shining like Angwussi's wing. I shall tie her hair in little braids like all married women's are; then my boy will give those clothes to her — those white things he has made. And when our Katchinas go back home, after Nimani, then our girl will wear all those new clothes ——'

She paused and looked at 'Yeshva and young Butterfly, who grinned at their parents and each other. They were not embarrassed by this talk; for why not welcome this new life that bounded gaily toward them and filled the air with joy?

Below, the feathered emblem of the Soyal god — the mark of a newborn life of song and dance and prayer — was powdered slowly by the falling flakes that fluttered from the sky.

THE END

Glossary OF HOPI WORDS

GLOSSARY OF HOPI WORDS

Aha. The name of the Soyal Katchina, chief deity from the south.
Ahöla. The Sun god of the Katchina Clan.
Akuka. Acoma pueblo in New Mexico.
Alosaka. The supreme deity of the Horn Clan.
Ancha'ai. It is right.
Angak'tchina. A bearded Katchina from the east.
Angwusnasumtaka. The crow-winged mother of the Floggers; the chief deity of the Squash Clan of Mishongnovi.
Anknwa. The series of night dances in the kivas in March.
Aototo. The highest ranking Katchina, introduced by the Kokop Clan.
Askwali. Thank you, a word used only by girls and women. *See* **Kwakwai.**
Atöeh. The red and white cloak worn by Hopi women.
Aya. A gourd rattle used in ceremonies.

Bahana. White man.

Castile. Spaniard.
Chil' Katchina. A deity named for the chili pods worn on his head.

Hahai'ih. The mother of the Katchinas bringing the snow and rain.
Hakami'i. Where do (you) go?
Haliksai. So it was in the beginning.
Hano. The Hopi name for the Tewa village.
Hanomana. Hopi name for a Tewa girl.
Hehea. An amorous god, chief of the Tewa Corn Clan.
Hemisi. Jemez pueblo in New Mexico.
Hemis Katchinam. The deities of the Niman ceremony, originating in Jemez.

Glossary OF HOPI WORDS

Hin. Where?

Ho-eh. An erotic personage appearing in the Powamu ceremony.

Höhua. A pompous figure who always walks or dances with his legs crossed.

Honankuku. Describing the paw of a badger.

Honanngamoki. Medicine bag of badger skin.

Honansoki. Badger claw.

Honanwüchti. Badger woman.

Hopi. Shortened form of the tribal name Hopitu Shinimu, the peaceful people.

Hovelo. Name representing the white stripe down a badger's face.

Hurungkwa. Bunched feather warrior symbol drawn back from top of mask.

Ichivuh. A name used for any of the angry Katchinas.

Isva. Coyote; also the name of the spring below the eastern mesa.

I-tam. We.

Kaeh. No.

Kahopi. Literally, 'not Hopi,' therefore 'bad.'

Kalavi. A green-faced chief Katchina never seen except in the kiva.

Katchina. The anthropomorphic masked conception of any of hundreds of powers from the sun to a desert plant.

Kavo. Tomorrow.

Kawaika. The pueblo of Laguna in New Mexico.

Keesa. The chicken hawk, or the Katchina representing it.

Kikmongwi. The village chief.

Kisi Shadow. A bowered structure frequently seen in New Mexico and in Hopi erected for the Snake Dance.

Kökelom. An irregular plural of Kokle.

Kokle. The kindly deity from Kisiuva, the Shadow Spring; usually he is the Katchina who gives presents to the children in the Powamu ceremony.

Kököinaka. The leader in a dance.

Kokozhori. The small spotted chief Katchina of the Corn Clan.

Kowako. Rooster.

Koyala. The black-and-white-striped ancestral shades of the Tewa.

Koyemsi. The 'Mudhead.' First man.

Kwahoya. 'Eagle-little-one.'

Kwakwai. Thank you; a word used only by men and boys. *See* **Askwali.**

Kwamana. The eagle girl.

Kwavöhuh. Eagle breast-feather.

Kwayeshva. Eagle alighted.

Lapöktuh. The imitator.

Letaiyo. Gray fox.

Letotovi. A Katchina in the racing ceremony who tries to smear his opponent with black corn smut.

Lolimuh. A plant believed, by its consumption, to ensure the birth of boys.

Lolomai. Good.

Löyi. Two.

Makya. Eagle hunter.

Manangaya. A green lizard or the Katchina representing it.

Maski. The shadowy abode of the dead.

Massauh. Skeleton man, first inhabitant of the earth's surface and guardian of the dead.

Mishongnovi. The most easterly of the middle mesa villages.

Mohu. Yucca.

Moosa. Cat.

Moos'hoya. Kitten.

Muyingwuh. The god of germination.

Nalöyi. Four.

Nanatashkamuh. Irregular plural of Natashka.

Nasumta. The 'squash-blossom' head-dress of a virgin.

Natashka. One of the huge-mouthed monsters appearing with Soyoko.

Navajo. The nomadic neighboring tribe living nearest the Hopi.

Nöhta. The hollow reed.

'Nömsi. Abbreviated form of Sikyanömsi.
Növanchichiklauca. The racing Katchina who tears shirts.
Növatükyaovi. The 'snow-high-place,' the San Francisco Peaks.

Öki. Am here.
Öm or **Öma.** You.
Oraibi. The first village of the western mesa.
Ösö. The buckthorn cactus.
Owangozhrozhro. The 'stone-devourer.'

Paho. A prayer plume, affixed to a small stick.
Paiyo. Three.
Palamootsta. A rock southwest of Mishongnovi on which is an eagle's nest and a shrine.
Pas. Very.
Patki. The name of the Cloud Clan from the south.
Pi'inya. A type of milkweed.
Piki. The parchment-like bread made of corn.
Pivani. The weasel.
Pohaha. The Tewa goddess of war.
Pöhsökinaya. Drummer.
Polakka. The Tewa name of a member of the Corn Clan.
Polimana. Butterfly girl.
Pong Katchina. The Snow god of the Tewa.
Pongkwiyo. Snow woman.
Potavi. The cotton strand that marks the path for the dead.
Powaka. An evil sorcerer.
Powamuya. The great annual ceremony of midwinter.

Quivi. Fancy.
Quivihoya. One who shows off.

Shalako. A huge deity of the Cloud Clan, arrayed in a conical dress of eagle feathers and appearing as a being nine to ten feet high.
Shongopavi. The most westerly of the middle mesa villages.
Shötüknanguh. The god of high zenith.
Sikyanömsi. Yellow flower.

Sio. The Hopi name for Zuni pueblo.
Sipapuni. The place of ancestral emergence. Called Sipapu in New Mexico.
Siskyap Katchina. The 'canyon' Katchina; a chief god of the Corn Clan.
Sitchumovi. The middle village of the eastern mesa.
Söevi. Ashes used in making *piki.*
Sohuh. Wild hay.
Someviki. Mush wrapped in corn husk.
Sosoyoktuh. Plural of Soyoko.
Sowüchti. Grandmother.
Soyala. The chief god of the Cloud Clan and the first deity to arrive in winter.
Soyoko. The witch whose cave is south of Mishongnovi.

Taka. Man.
Talatömsi. The goddess of the dawn.
Talavai. The early morning; also the Katchina named for it.
Tangaka. Rainbow in the Tewa language.
Tavu. The rabbit.
Tawa. The sun.
Tchavaiyo. An ogre of Tewa origin.
Tchökapölöluh. A small mud-slinging Katchina of the racing group.
Tchua. The rattlesnake.
Tewa. The name of the pueblo people of the most easternly Hopi village; also the name of their kinsmen in New Mexico.
Tiposi. A small boy.
Toriva. The spring below Mishongnovi.
Totcha. The humming-bird.
Tsañwadi. The ancestral home of the Tewa of Hano on the Santa Cruz River in New Mexico.
Tsapele. Tewa name meaning 'white girl.'
Tsoshbushnaka. The one having turquoise earrings.
Tühkaita. Third person singular of the verb to speak.
Tuma'eh. Let us go.
Tunguf Katchina. The flogging god of the initiation ceremony.

Utseh. The Hopi name for the Ute Indians.

Wawas Katchinam. The racing gods.
Wehuhuh. A lazy god who accompanies the witch Soyoko.
Wi. Yes.
Wiki. A connected series of rolls of *piki* for ceremonial presentation.
Wisoko. The buzzard.
Wuwuchim. The fall ritual of initiation into the four great societies.

'Yeshva. Abbreviated form of Kwayeshva.
Yungya'ai. Come in.
Yupngna. A medicine herb.

Plates

I

SIKYANÖMSI, HER YOUNGER SISTER, LITTLE FLUTE GIRL AND THE CRADLED 'YESHVA

II

'YESHVA AND HIS GRANDMOTHERS

III

KWAVÖHUH LISTENS AS MAKYA TELLS THE MEANING OF KATCHINA DOLLS

IV

MAKYA DRINKS THE COOL WATER FROM TORIVA

MAKYA, THE GRANDFATHER V

SOWÜCHTI, THE GRANDMOTHER VI

VII *Painting by Kabotie*

THE KÖKELOM GIVING PRESENTS TO THE CHILDREN

THE ARRIVAL OF THE DREADED SOSOYUKTUH

VIII *Painting by Kabotie*

Painting by Quoyavema

IX

THE FLIGHT OF THE BOGEYMEN

EAGLE'S NEST AT PALAMOOTSTA

X

XI

'YESHVA'S GODFATHER WEARS THE SACRED BREASTFEATHER

AHÖLA, THE SUN-FATHER

XII *Painting by Kabotie*

ANGWUSNASUMTAKA, THE CROW-WINGED MOTHER

XIII

ainting by Quoyavema

XIV

THE FLOGGING RITUAL IN THE UNDERGROUND KIVA

XV

TCHA, THE HUMMING BIRD

Painting by Mootzka

XVI

POLIMANA, THE BUTTERFLY GIRL OF HANO

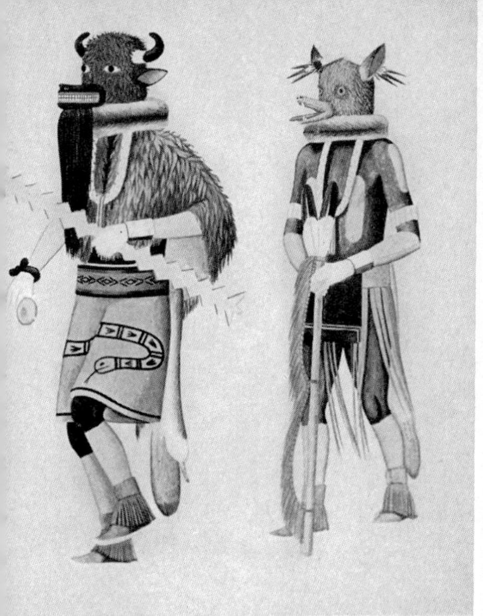

ainting by Mootzka XVII

THE BUFFALO AND FOX KATCHINAS

Painting by Kabotie XVIII

TCHAKWAINA, THE WARRIOR GOD OF THE ASA CLAN

LETAIYO

XIX

XX MAHLE

XXI THE TEWA FAMILY

'YESHVA RIDING TOWARD HANO XXII

'YESHVA XXIII

XXIV

'YESHVA AND BUTTERFLY GIRL, TINY DOTS ON THE MIGHTY MESA

ainting by Quoyavema

XXV

PALALÖKONG, THE PLUMED SERPENT, DESTROYS AN ANCIENT TOWN

WHEN THE FLOOD HAS ENGULFED THE TOWN

ainting by Quoyavema

XXVI

XXVII

Painting by Quoyavem

THE KÖKELOM LEAVE THE KIVA AS AHÖLA AND THE CHIEF GODS ENTER

THE KATCHINAS SWARM ABOUT THE ANCIENT TOWN OF SHONGOPAVI

XXVIII

Painting by Kabot

Painting by Kabotie

XXIX

THE EAGLE DANCE

THE MOUNTAIN SHEEP DANCE

Painting by Kabotie

XXX

XXXI *Painting by Kaboti*

THE CLOUD-SYMBOLLED SHALAKO AND HIS SISTER WITH HAHAI, THE MOTHER OF THE GODS BRINGING RAIN

'YESHVA RIDES INTO HANO XXXII

'YESHVA AND BUTTERFLY GIRL

XXXIV

'NÖMSI'S YOUNGEST SISTER

Painting by Kabotie XXXV

HÖHMSONA AND THE RACING GODS

THE NIMAN CEREMONY

Painting by Kabotie XXXVI

XXXVII

Painting by Quoyavema

THE DAWN RITUAL OF THE GOD'S FAREWELL

Painting by Kabotie

XXXVIII

THE SNAKE DANCE

THE SUMMER BUTTERFLY DANCE AT HANO

XXXIX

XL

Painting by Mootzka

HE-EH-EH, THE WARRIOR MAIDEN, AND THE GODS OF PACHAVA

SUN GODS, ANGRY GODS, BIRD GODS AND ANIMAL GODS SWARM ABOUT THE PACHAVA CELEBRATING TOWN

XLI

Painting by Mootzka

Painting by Quoyavema

XLII

AOTATO, THE CROW-WINGED MOTHER, THE FLOGGERS AND OTHER GREAT KATCHINAS LEAD THE PACHAVA PROCESSION

WALPI, WHERE MAN FOUGHT, PRAYED AND DANCED FOR RAIN

XLIII

LXIV

THE CHIEFS DEFEATED BY THE SUN'S UNCEASING ANGER AND THE PLUMED SERPENT'S MALICE, MEET IN THE KIVA

MAKYA, ON WHOSE SHOULDERS RESTS THE GROWING BURDEN OF HIS PEOPLE

LXV

XLVI

THE CHIEFS SEARCH THEIR MINDS FOR MEANS TO APPEASE THE SUN AND THE SERPENT OF THE LOWER WORLD

XLVII

THE TOWN CRIER, THE CHA'AKMONGWI, WHOSE VOICE CUTS THROUGH THE WAVING HEAT OF DESERT SAND

XLVIII

BUTTERFLY GIRL AND THE DROUGHT-KILLED DESERT

A FEW ELUSIVE CLOUDS PASS OVER THE WIND-TOSSED SAND

XLIX

L

THE VILLAGE CHIEF SEES THE RAIN WALKING WHILE THE SKY GOD'S SPEAR ANNIHILATES THE DROUGHT

LI

'THEN I SHALL TAKE THOSE WHEELS OF HERS AND BRUSH EACH HAIR AND LET IT FALL IN SOME BOWL OF SUDS'

'IT WILL BE SUCH FUN, YOU AND I WILL FIGHT WITH MUD AND YOUR SISTERS WITH MY MOTHER'S GIRLS'

LII

LIII

THE DAY OF WHICH TWO MOTHERS DREAM

LIV

TAWA, THE SUN, GOES TO SLEEP IN THE GREAT CLOUD HOUSES OF THE WEST